D1416185

ADVENTURES

Senior Author
William K. Durr

Senior Coordinating Author
John J. Pikulski

Coordinating Authors
Rita M. Bean
J. David Cooper
Nicholas A. Glaser
M. Jean Greenlaw
Hugh Schoephoerster

Authors
Mary Lou Alsin
Kathryn Au
Rosalinda B. Barrera
Joseph E. Brzeinski
Ruth P. Bunyan
Jacqueline C. Comas
Frank X. Estrada
Robert L. Hillerich
Timothy G. Johnson
Pamela A. Mason
Joseph S. Renzulli

HOUGHTON MIFFLIN COMPANY BOSTON

Atlanta Dallas Geneva, Illinois Palo Alto Princeton Toronto

Acknowledgments

For each of the selections listed below, grateful acknowledgment is made for permission to adapt and/or reprint original or copyrighted material, as follows:

"The Balancing Girl," adapted from *The Balancing Girl,* by Berniece Rabe. Copyright © 1981 by Berniece Rabe. Reprinted by permission of the publisher E. P. Dutton, Inc. and McIntosh and Otis, Inc.

"The Case of the Missing Code Book," adapted from *The Case of the Stolen Code Book,* by Barbara Rinkoff. Text Copyright © 1971 by Barbara Rinkoff. Reprinted by permission of Crown Publishers, Inc.

"Castles," adapted from *That Was Summer,* by Marci Ridlon. Copyright © 1969 by Marci Ridlon. Reprinted by permission of the author.

"First Day of School," from *I Wonder How, I Wonder Why,* by Aileen Fisher. Copyright © 1962 by Aileen Fisher. Reprinted by permission of the author.

"The Garden," adapted from *Frog and Toad Together* (pages 18–29), written and illustrated by Arnold Lobel. (An *I Can Read Book*) Copyright © 1971, 1972 by Arnold Lobel. Reprinted by permission of Harper & Row, Publishers, Inc. and World's Work Ltd. First published in Great Britain in 1973 by World's Work.

Continued on page 304.

Printed in the U.S.A.
ISBN: 0-395-43681-8

DEFGHIJ-D-943210/89

Contents

Magazine One

Magazine Two

Magazine Three

Adventures
Magazine One

Contents

Stories

Content Selection

Poems

Skills

Vocabulary

The New Girl at School

by Judy Delton

Marcia is going to a new school. Find out how Marcia feels about her new school.

My mother got a new job today. I got a new school.

"It will be fun," said my mother. "You will make many new friends."

When I walked into school, everyone stared. Everyone was with a friend but me.

I had on my new shirt with the grasshopper on it. (No one even looked at the grasshopper.)

The children called me Martha. (My name is Marcia.)

Everyone knew where the lunchroom was. (I had to ask.)

Everyone could do subtraction. (I was the only one who couldn't.)

"I don't like this school," I said to my mother that night.

"It will get better," she said.

The next day I went to school on the bus. (The seats were for two. No one sat with me.)

In the lunch line, everyone was with a friend. (I was the only one by myself.)

"Today was no better," I said to my mother that night. "I don't like being the new girl at school."

"Give it time," said my mother.

On Wednesday, I didn't want to go to school. I said I had the mumps. I said I'd run away.

My mother said, "You have to get on the bus."

At school we drew some pictures. The teacher held some of them up. (She didn't hold up my picture.)

After lunch we played "Captain-May-I." (I wasn't the captain.) But when we played baseball, I made it to second base.

That night my mother asked, “How was school?”

“Give it time,” I said.

“Maybe I should talk to the teacher,” she said.

“You don’t need to do that,” I said.

On Thursday, we made airplanes. The teacher put mine up. (Just mine.)

I had on my grasshopper shirt and someone asked, “Is that a tadpole?”

I said, “No, it’s a grasshopper.”

Karen asked me to sleep over at her house. (She could only ask two.)

On Friday, my mother said, "You *could* stay with Grandma, and go to your old school."

"Why?" I asked. "I'm used to this school now and do you know what? There was a new girl at school today, and she doesn't understand subtraction."

Story Wrap-up

Summary Questions

At first, Marcia did not like her new school. Tell what happened to make her feelings change. The questions will help you.

1. What happened to Marcia on her first day at the new school? How did she feel?
2. Do you think one day was enough time to start liking a new school? Tell why.
3. What happened after lunch on Wednesday? How did Marcia feel then?

4. Draw pictures of Marcia at the beginning of the story and at the end of the story. Tell why Marcia's feelings changed.

The Reading and Writing Connection

At the end of the story, there was another new girl at school. Pretend you are Marcia. Write what you could say or do to help the new girl. Choose some of the words in the box to help you.

subtraction	**captain**	**stare**
understand	**baseball**	**airplanes**

FIRST DAY AT SCHOOL

by Aileen Fisher

I wonder
if my drawing
will be as good as theirs.

I wonder
if they'll like me
or just be full of stares.

I wonder
if my teacher
will look like Mom or Gram.

I wonder
if my puppy
will wonder
where I am.

GREGORY, The Terrible Eater

by Mitchell Sharmat

Mother and Father Goat think Gregory is a terrible eater. Can Gregory eat the foods he likes *and* make his mother and father happy?

Once there was a goat named Gregory. Gregory liked to kick up his legs and jump from rock to rock.

Gregory thought he was just like any other goat, but he wasn't. Gregory was a terrible eater. Every time he sat down to eat with his mother and father, he knew he would have a problem.

"Would you like a tin can, Gregory?" asked Mother Goat.

"No, thanks," said Gregory.

"How about an old box?" asked Father Goat.

"Baaaaaa," said Gregory.

"Well, I think this is a great supper for a goat," said Mother Goat, as she picked up an old shoe.

"I think so, too," said Father Goat. "I don't know why you don't like these things, Gregory. You are too picky."

"I'm not picky," said Gregory. "I just want things like vegetables, and fish, and bread to eat. Good things like that."

Mother Goat put down the shoe she was eating. "Now what kind of supper is *that,* Gregory?" she asked.

"It's what I like," said Gregory.

"It's terrible," said Father Goat.

After Gregory left the table, Father Goat said, "Gregory is a terrible eater."

The next morning Mother and Father Goat were having some old pants and a coat for breakfast.

Gregory came to the table.

"Good morning, Gregory," said Father and Mother Goat.

"Good morning," said Gregory. "May I have orange juice, eggs, and bread for breakfast?"

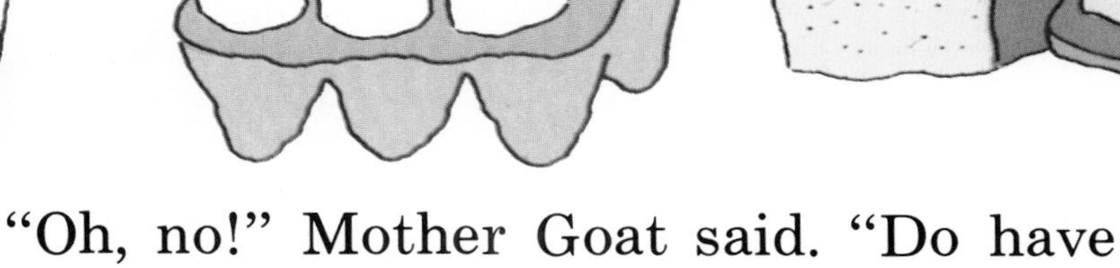

"Oh, no!" Mother Goat said. "Do have some of this coat."

"Take a little of these pants," said Father Goat.

"Baaaaaa," said Gregory and he left the table.

Father Goat threw down his napkin. "That does it!" he said. "Gregory just isn't eating right. We must do something."

Father and Mother Goat took Gregory to see Dr. Ram.

"What's the problem?" Dr. Ram asked, when he had finished the old box he was eating.

"Gregory is a terrible eater," said Mother Goat.

"We've given him the best – shoes, pants, boxes, tin cans, coats. But all he wants are fruits, vegetables, eggs, fish, bread, and other terrible things."

"What do you have to say about all of this, Gregory?" asked Dr. Ram.

"I want what I like," said Gregory.

"I see," said Dr. Ram. He turned to Mother and Father Goat. "I've helped picky eaters before," he said. "They have to learn to like good food slowly. Give Gregory just one new food to try each day."

That night for supper Mother Goat gave Gregory spaghetti. In the spaghetti, she put an old shoelace.

"This is pretty good," said Gregory.

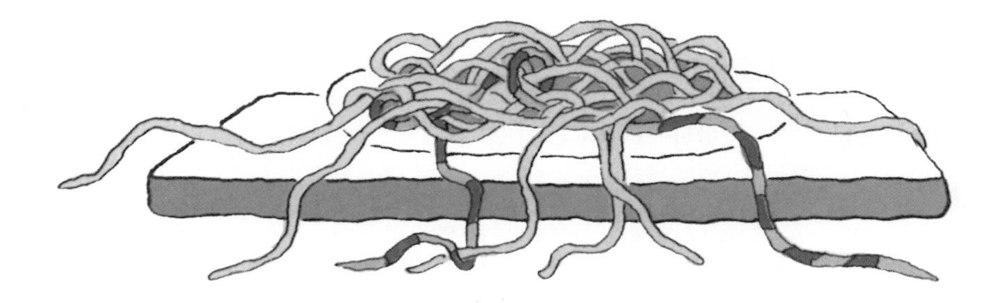

The next day she gave him some vegetables and a rubber heel to eat. She cut up the heel for him.

"That was good," said Gregory.

The day after that, Mother Goat said, "Today we have something that I know you're going to like – vegetable soup. But if you eat the soup, you must eat the can, too."

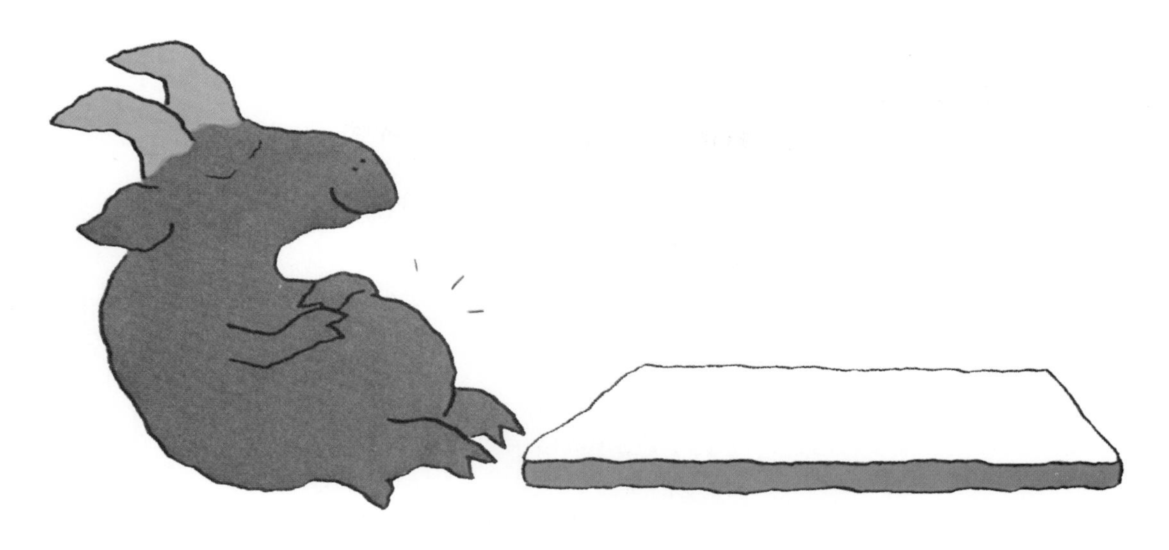

"Yum, Yum," said Gregory.

"Now you're starting to eat like a goat," said Father Goat.

"I'm learning to like everything," said Gregory.

One evening, Father Goat asked, "Has anyone seen my cap?"

"I haven't," said Mother Goat. "Come to think of it, I haven't seen my slippers today."

Father Goat turned to Gregory and said, "Gregory, did you eat my cap and your mother's slippers?"

"Yes," said Gregory. "I can't help it. Now I like everything."

"Well," said Mother Goat, "it's all right to eat like a goat, but you shouldn't eat like a pig."

"Oh," said Gregory.

After Gregory went to bed, Mother Goat said to Father Goat, "Gregory's eating too much. We'll have to do something about it."

The next evening, just before supper, Mother and Father Goat went to the dump.

They found some flat tires, a violin, and part of a car. They took everything home and left it in front of the house.

When Gregory came home, he saw all the things in front of the house. "What's all this?" he asked.

"This is your supper," said Father Goat.

"It all looks good," said Gregory.

Gregory ate the tires and the violin.
But when he started in on the car, he said,
"I don't feel well. I'm going to my room."

"I think Gregory had too much to eat,"
said Father Goat.

"I hope so," said Mother Goat.

All night, Gregory moaned and groaned. The next morning when he went down for breakfast, he was feeling better.

"What would you like for breakfast today, Gregory?" asked Father Goat.

"Three eggs, two napkins, and a glass of orange juice," said Gregory.

"I think that's just about right," said Mother Goat.

And it was.

Story Wrap-up

Summary Questions

At first, Gregory was a picky eater. By the end of the story, Gregory wasn't so picky. These questions will help you tell how this happened.

1. How was Gregory different from other goats?
2. Where did Mother Goat and Father Goat take Gregory? Do you think Dr. Ram's ideas worked? Why?
3. When did Mother say that Gregory was eating "just about right"? What did she mean? How did she feel?
4. Some people might think this story was very funny. What do you think? Why?

The Reading and Writing Connection

The words in the lists below name some things Gregory ate.

vegetables	**violin**
fruits	**pair of pants**
spaghetti	**shoelaces**
eggs	**rubber heel**

The lists are not alike, are they?

Pretend you are Gregory. Write a note asking a friend to come for dinner. Tell about the things you will have.

Use some of the words from both lists in your note.

Skill

Drawing Conclusions

Many times in your reading, the author will tell you some things and let you figure out other things for yourself.

Read the story below.

Mark wanted to know more about elephants.

"I think I will go and get a book about elephants," he said.

Mark looked at all the books on the shelf. Finally he found just the book he was looking for.

Mark handed the book and a card to a woman. The woman looked at the card. Then she handed the book and the card back to Mark.

She said, "You should bring this book back in two weeks."

You know that Mark might have found the book at his house, at a bookstore, or at the library. Thinking about what you read may help you to figure out where Mark went to get the book.

The woman said Mark could keep the book for two weeks. You know that if Mark had gotten the book from his house or from a bookstore, no one would say how long he could keep it. But if Mark had gotten the book at the library, he probably could keep it for only two weeks.

Thinking about all of these things helps you to know that Mark must have gotten the book from the library even though the author did not say that.

Now read this story.

Every morning Karen fills her bird feeder with seeds. Every day when Karen comes home from school, the seeds are gone.

"I'm glad Father made a tall bird feeder," said Karen. "If it weren't so tall, other animals might eat the seeds."

One Saturday morning Karen took the seeds out to the feeder. Later that day, she looked out the window thinking she would see birds at the feeder. Instead of birds, Karen saw squirrels! The squirrels were at the top of the feeder eating the seeds.

Which of these sentences is true?

1. Father made a tall feeder so the squirrels could get to the seeds.
2. Karen was surprised to see the squirrels.
3. Karen doesn't like birds.

Tell why you think this.

Skill Summary

Remember, you can figure out some things for yourself when you read. Use what the author says and what you know yourself.

THE FUNNY FAROLA

by Ann Miranda with María Guerrero

Farolas are lanterns that are used to give light. Find out how a very special farola helps Rosa and Ramón.

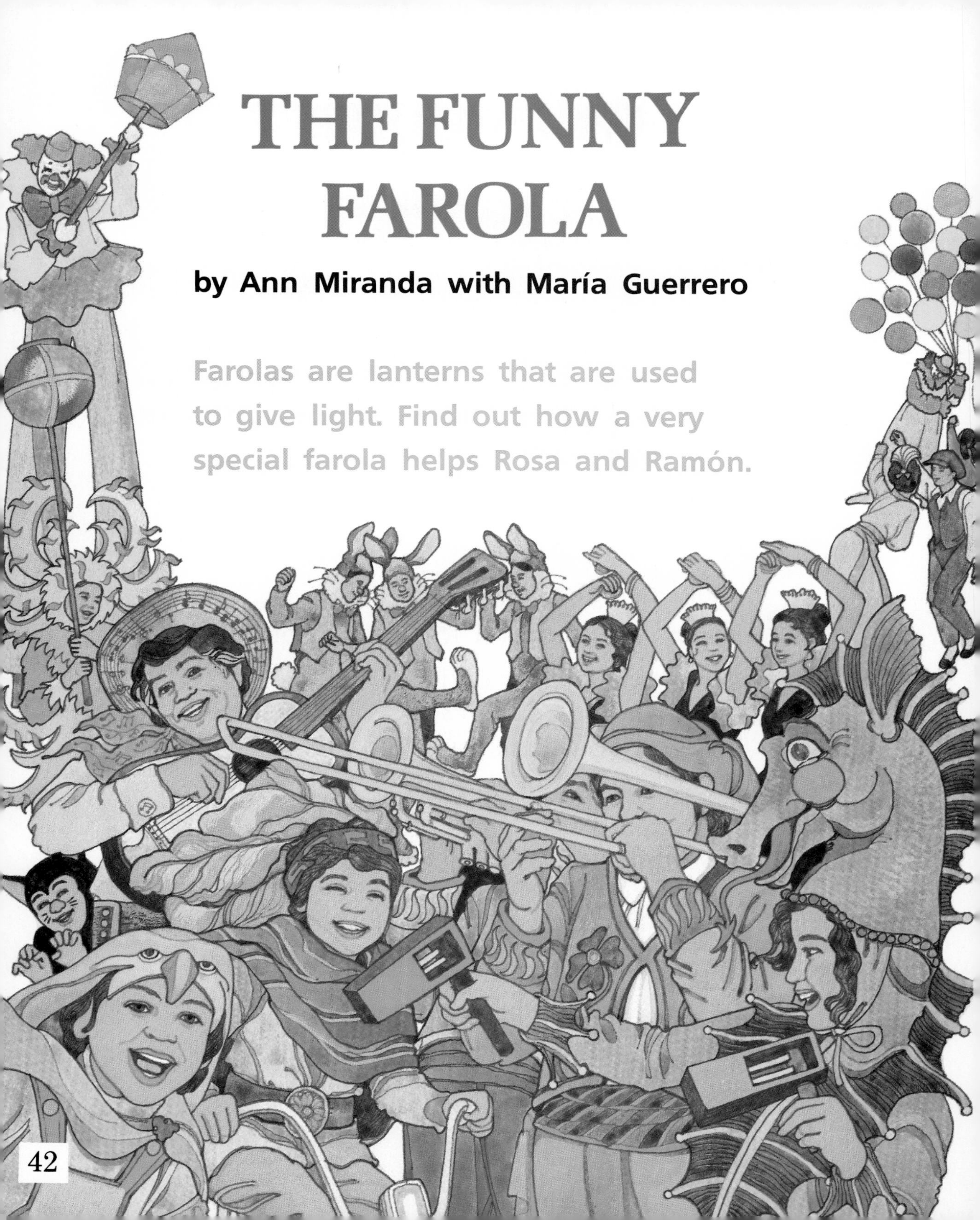

Dora Rivera lived with her Mamá and Papá, her sister Rosa, and her brother Ramón. Mr. and Mrs. Rivera owned a flower store, but today the flower store was closed. It was the day of the big parade.

The parade was a time for having fun. It was a time for singing and dancing. It was a time for farolas and funny costumes. Dora and her family were going to the parade in costumes that made them look like the flowers and plants in the flower store.

"I'll just get a new candle for my farola and we'll be all ready to go," said Papá.

"Wait! I have to get something, too," cried Dora as she ran out of the room. When she came back, she was smiling and holding a long stick with a frog at the top.

"What's that?" asked Ramón.

"It's a farola!" said Dora. "I made it all by myself."

Rosa and Ramón looked at each other and laughed.

"That's not a farola," laughed Rosa.

"Papá has a farola," said Ramón. "All you have is a frog! Everyone will laugh at you if you take that funny-looking frog to the parade."

This was not at all what Dora had expected. She wondered if Ramón and Rosa were right. She decided to take her farola to the parade anyway.

When Dora arrived at the parade she didn't know what to look at first, but she knew right away what it was that made the parade so much fun. It was the funny costumes and the happy songs and dances.

The smell of fresh fruits and vegetables was everywhere. Dora loved listening to the happy sounds of laughter that were all around her.

"Oh, Papá," said Dora. "I love the parade. We are going to have so much fun today."

"Yes," said Papá. "I am sure that we will. I have never seen so many people!"

"We must stay close together so that no one gets lost," said Mamá.

"We will, Mamá," said Rosa. "We won't get lost."

"Now," said Papá, "let's join the others in the dancing."

Dora had never had so much fun. She forgot about Rosa and Ramón making fun of her farola. As she danced, she waved it all around. More and more people joined in the dancing. Soon there were groups of flowers and plants and rabbits. How funny they looked!

Rosa and Ramón were having so much fun that they forgot all about staying close to Mamá and Papá. Holding hands, they danced and danced. They didn't know that as they danced, they were moving farther and farther away from Mamá and Papá.

All of a sudden, Rosa looked around the crowd. "Ramón!" she shouted. "Where's Mamá? Where's Papá?"

"I can't see them," cried Ramón. "There are too many people!"

"Which way should we go?" asked Rosa.

At the same time that Rosa and Ramón were deciding which way to go, Mamá and Papá were looking for them.

Papá said, "Come here, Dora. Hop up onto my shoulders and see if you can find Rosa and Ramón."

Dora hopped up onto her Papá's shoulders. Still waving her farola, she looked all around the crowd. She did not see Rosa and Ramón, but Rosa saw Dora's farola waving over the crowd.

"Ramón, Ramón!" Rosa shouted. "Look! Isn't that Dora's farola?"

"Yes, it is!" said Ramón. "Now we know where Mamá and Papá are."

With the funny-looking frog to show the way, Rosa and Ramón slowly made their way back.

"Oh, Dora," said Rosa. "We were lost and we didn't know which way to go. It was the frog on your farola that helped us."

"It's a good thing that you didn't listen to me," said Ramón. "Now I know that your farola was not so funny after all!"

Dora smiled.

Story Wrap-up

Summary Questions

Rosa and Ramón thought Dora's farola was too funny-looking to take to the parade. Tell what happened to change their minds. These questions will help you.

1. What did Dora's farola look like?
2. Why did Rosa and Ramón get lost at the parade?
3. What happened after Dora hopped onto Papa's shoulders?
4. If Rosa and Ramón had not seen Dora's farola, what could they have done to find their way back? What would you have done?

The Reading and Writing Connection

Suppose you are meeting Dora at the parade.

What will you wear?
Will your eyes and mouth be painted?
Will your feet look funny?

Write a note to Dora telling her where to meet you and what you will look like.

Use the words in the box to help you write your note.

parade	**arrive**	**farola**	**wave**
costume	**join**	**shoulders**	**crowd**

Vocabulary

Telling More

Suppose you went to a parade and saw the clown in the picture at the right. If you wanted to tell someone about the clown, the sentence below tells what you might say.

I saw a clown in the parade.

This sentence tells what you saw, but it doesn't tell very much about the clown. The sentence below tells more.

> I saw a funny clown
> with blue hair and long
> legs dancing in the parade.

This sentence tells how the clown looked and what the clown was doing. This sentence gives a clearer picture of what you saw.

Think of some words you might use to tell about the picture above. The words below may help you.

huge	**water**	**funny**
blue	**skates**	**dancers**
tiny	**clown**	**jump**

Reading in Social Studies

What Could You Be?

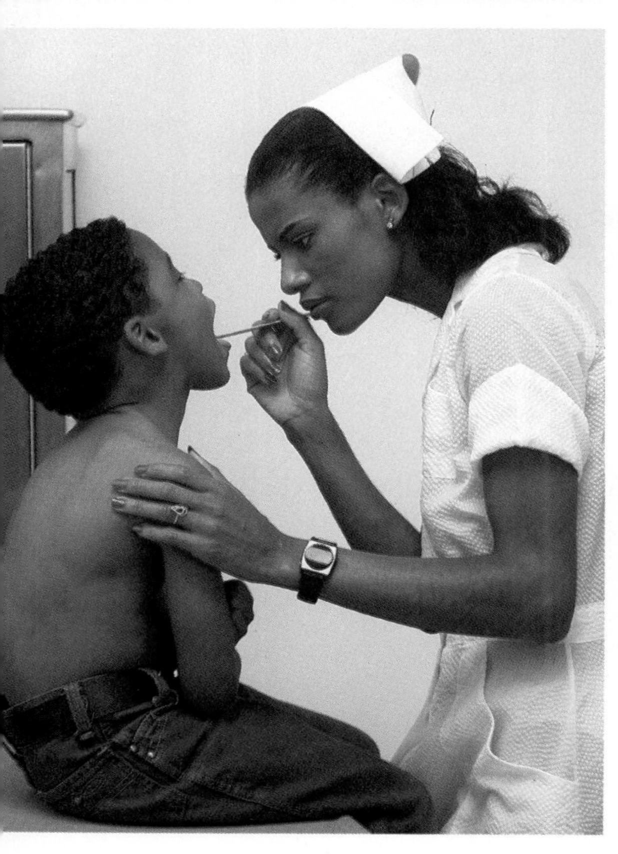

There are many things that you could be when you grow up. Do you have any ideas about what you want to be? How will you decide?

What could you be when you grow up? You can choose from so many things. Think about the things you like to do now.

Do you like to grow things? When you grow up, you could grow things in a greenhouse. You could grow different kinds of flowers, or you might grow plants that people eat.

Do you like animals? Maybe you would like to be a veterinarian and take care of pets or other animals. Maybe you would like to work with animals in a zoo.

Do you like computers? If you do, you might want to be a programmer and write programs for the computer. A program is a set of directions that tells the computer what to do.

Maybe you like to help others learn about new things. If you do, you could be a teacher.

What things do you do well? Are you good at sports? If you are, you might make your living by playing a sport. You might show other people how to play a sport, or you might like to work in a store that sells things to people who play sports.

Are you learning how to play a musical instrument? By the time you grow up, you may play so well that people will come to hear you play. Maybe you will decide to be a music teacher and help others learn to play.

Think about the grown-ups you know. What do they do? Do you want to be like one of them? Which one? What does that person do?

When you grow up, there are so many things you can be, it may be hard for you to choose.

Here are some questions you might think about now and as you grow older:

What do you like to do now?

What are you good at doing?

What does a grown-up that you want to be like do?

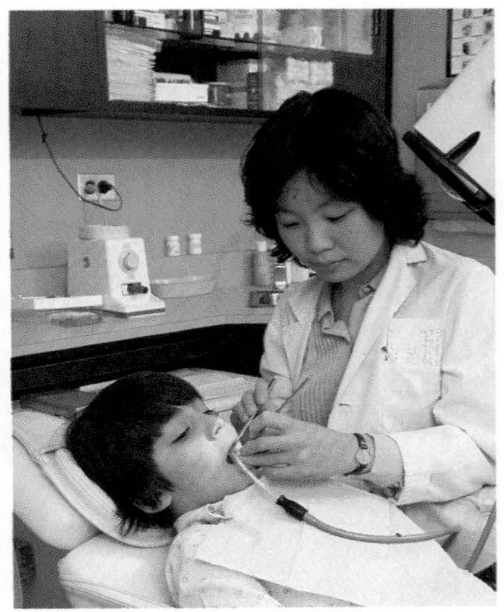

Story Wrap-up

Summary Questions

What would you like to be when you grow up? These questions can help you decide.

1. What is one thing you like to do now?
2. Do you know a grown-up who has a job you might like? What is that job?
3. You can give a friend some ideas about how to choose a job. What three things would you tell your friend to think about?

The Reading and Writing Connection

These words name things you can be.

veterinarian	**computer programmer**
music teacher	**greenhouse worker**

Would you choose one of these jobs? Write about a job and tell why you like it.

Skill

Summarizing

When you tell someone about a story, you do not have to tell everything that happens in the story. You only need to tell *some* of the things that happen.

Most stories are alike in some ways.

1. They tell about someone or something.
2. They take place somewhere.
3. Something happens to begin the story.
4. This causes something else to happen.
5. Something happens to end the story.

When you tell about a story, if you tell these five things you will be telling what the story is about.

Read the story on the next page. As you read, think about the five things that can be found in most stories.

Grasshopper and Ant

One lovely morning, Grasshopper walked outside his house in the cornfield and saw Ant. Ant was carrying food from the cornfield into his house.

"Ant," called Grasshopper. "Stop working so hard. Come and sit with me."

"Oh, no," said Ant. "I must store up food for the winter. You should be doing that, too."

"Not I," said Grasshopper. "You are silly to work so hard. It is such a lovely day, that I don't want to even *think* about winter."

So Ant went on working, and Grasshopper went on sitting. When winter came Ant had all the food he needed, but Grasshopper had none.

This story is about Grasshopper and Ant. The story takes place in a cornfield. What is the first important thing that happens? What happens next? How does the story end?

If you wanted to tell someone about this story, this is what you might say:

"Grasshopper and Ant were in the cornfield. Grasshopper told Ant to stop working and come and sit in the sun. Ant told Grasshopper that he should be storing up food for the winter. Grasshopper went on sitting, and Ant went on working. When winter came, Ant had food, but Grasshopper had none."

If you told someone just this much, you would be telling the most important things about the story.

Here is another story for you to read.

Crow and the Cheese

One morning Crow and Fox both saw a piece of cheese at the same time. Crow got to the cheese first. She picked it up and took it to the top of a tree.

"My dear Crow," called Fox. "I have heard that you are a wonderful singer. Won't you please sing a song for me?"

Crow didn't stop to think. She just opened her mouth, and out fell the cheese!

Fox smiled, picked up the cheese, and ate it all up!

If you wanted to tell someone about this story, what would you say?

Skill Summary

Remember, when you are telling about a story, think about the five important things listed on page 62.

"The Garden" From *Frog and Toad Together*

written and illustrated by Arnold Lobel

Frog gives Toad some flower seeds and tells Toad that gardening is hard work.

Toad finds out how hard it is when he tries to get the seeds to grow.

When Frog and Toad say that gardening is hard work, are they thinking about the same kind of work?

The Garden

Written and illustrated by Arnold Lobel

Frog was in his garden.

Toad came walking by.

"What a fine garden you have, Frog," he said.

"Yes," said Frog. "It is very nice, but it was hard work."

"I wish I had a garden," said Toad.

"Here are some flower seeds. Plant them in the ground," said Frog, "and soon you will have a garden."

"How soon?" asked Toad.

"Quite soon," said Frog.

Toad ran home.

He planted the flower seeds.

"Now, seeds," said Toad, "start growing."

Toad walked up and down a few times.

The seeds did not start to grow.

Toad put his head close to the ground and said, "Now, seeds, start growing!"

Toad looked at the ground again.

The seeds did not start to grow.

Toad put his head very close to the ground and shouted, "*NOW, SEEDS, START GROWING!*"

Frog came running up the path.

"What is going on?" he asked.

"My seeds will not grow," said Toad.

"You are shouting too much," said Frog. "Your seeds are afraid to grow."

"My seeds are afraid to grow?" asked Toad.

"Yes," said Frog. "Leave them alone for a few days. Let the sun shine on them. Let the rain fall on them. Soon your seeds will start to grow."

That night Toad looked out of his window.

"My seeds have not started to grow," said Toad. "They must be afraid of the dark."

Toad went out to his garden with some candles.

"I will read the seeds a story," said Toad. "Then they will not be afraid."

Toad read a long story to his seeds.

All the next day Toad sang songs to his seeds.

And all the next day Toad read poems to his seeds.

And all the next day Toad played music for his seeds.

Toad looked at the ground.

The seeds still did not start to grow.

"What shall I do?" cried Toad. "These seeds must be very frightened!"

Then Toad was so tired that he fell asleep.

"Toad, Toad, wake up," said Frog. "Look at your garden!"

Toad looked at his garden.

Little green plants were coming up out of the ground.

"At last," shouted Toad, "my seeds have stopped being afraid to grow!"

"Now you will have a nice garden, too," said Frog.

"Yes," said Toad, "but you were right, Frog. It was very hard work."

Story Wrap-up

Summary Questions

Frog and Toad worked in different ways. The questions will help you tell about them.

1. What did Frog tell Toad to do with his seeds?
2. Why did Toad do different things instead?
3. What do you think Frog meant when he said gardening was hard work? What do you think Toad meant?

The Reading and Writing Connection

Pretend your garden will grow if you talk to it. Write about what you will say to it. Use some of the words in the box.

quite	**afraid**	**shine**	**frightened**
shall	**few**	**rain**	**sun**

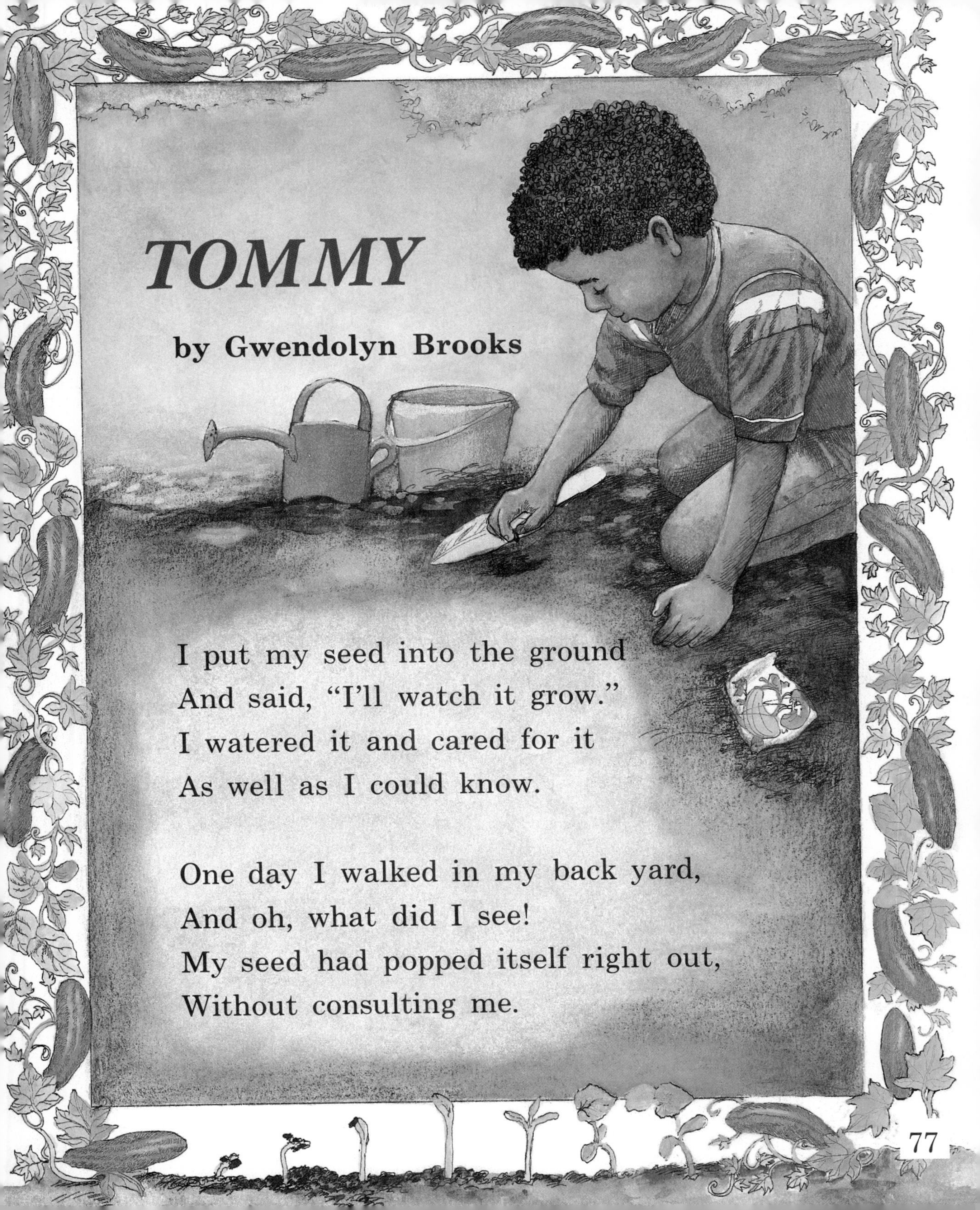

TOMMY

by Gwendolyn Brooks

I put my seed into the ground
And said, "I'll watch it grow."
I watered it and cared for it
As well as I could know.

One day I walked in my back yard,
And oh, what did I see!
My seed had popped itself right out,
Without consulting me.

Magazine Wrap-up

Do You Remember?

Finish the sentences below.

Marcia didn't like the new school until ...

Gregory wouldn't eat the things his mother and father ate until ...

Rosa and Ramón thought the farola that Dora made was silly until ...

Word Watch

Find a word in Group A to go with a word in Group B. Tell why you think the words go together.

Group A	**Group B**
mumps	**candle**
farola	**animal**
computer	**sick**
veterinarian	**program**

A Favorite Story

Write some sentences to tell about the story you liked best in Magazine One. Here are some things you might want to tell.

- Who was in the story?
- Where did the story take place?
- What was the first thing that happened?
- What happened next?
- How did the story end?

Books to Enjoy 

I Never Win! by Judy Delton

Charlie has a surprise for everyone.

Leo, Zack, and Emmie by Amy Ehrlich

Leo and Zack want to be Emmie's friend.

Days with Frog and Toad by Arnold Lobel

Two very good friends find that sometimes it's good to be alone.

Adventures

Magazine Two

Contents

Stories

Content Selection

Poems and Article

Skills

Vocabulary

The BALANCING Girl

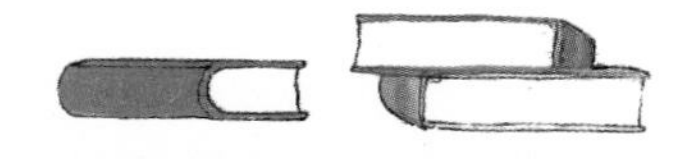

by Berniece Rabe

Margaret is very good at balancing things. Find out about the very special way that Margaret uses her balancing skills.

Margaret was very good at balancing. She could balance a book on her head. She could roll around in her wheelchair and the book would not fall off.

She could even balance herself and hop with her crutches.

At school, Margaret balanced all the picture cards on a table without any of them falling. Mr. Joliet said, "You have a very careful hand, Margaret."

Tommy said, "Anyone can do that."

Right then, with Tommy watching, Margaret started balancing blocks. She balanced ten blocks one on top of the other.

"That's easy," he said.

"Then you do it," said Margaret.

But Tommy wouldn't try. He just said, "I still say it's easy."

Margaret thought and thought. She wanted to do something that Tommy could not call easy.

It took a long time and great care, but at last Margaret finished a fine tower made by balancing blocks on top of each other.

Jean and William thought the tower was great, but Tommy said, "That's easy. I make towers like that at home all the time."

Margaret would have shouted at him if Mr. Joliet had not said, "It's time to go to the library."

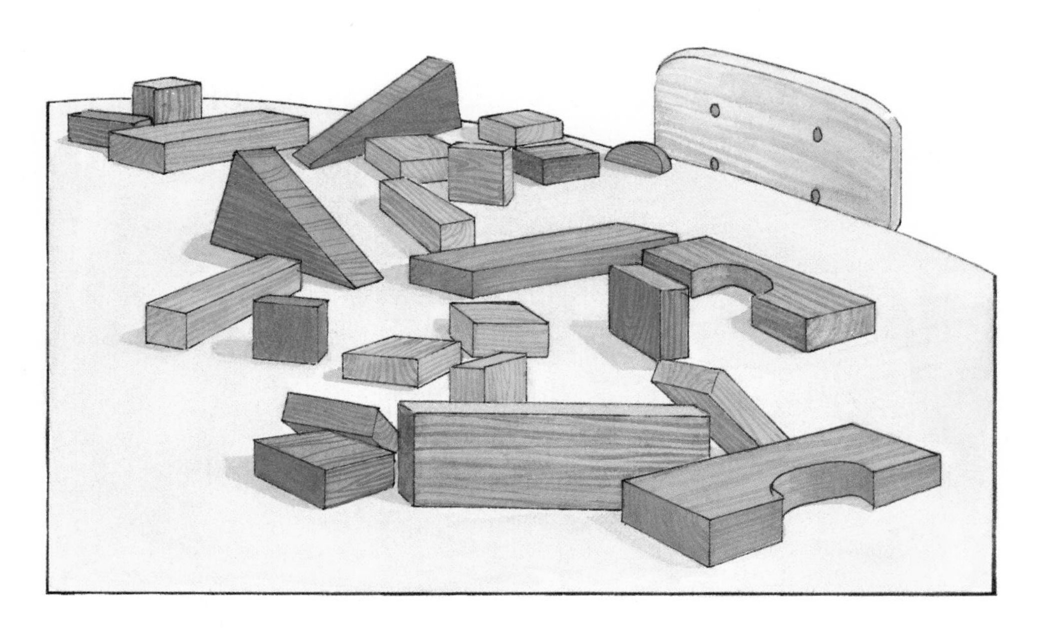

When they came back from the library, Margaret's tower was all over the table. It had been flattened out!

Tommy shouted, "Don't look at me! *I* don't know who did it!"

"*I* know who did it, and I don't want you to do it again!" said Margaret.

Just then, Mrs. Howard, the principal, walked into the room.

Mrs. Howard said, "We are going to hold a school carnival. We will use the money we make for books for the library. We need ideas for ways to make money."

Tommy said, "At my big brother's school carnival, he and my dad ran a fishpond. They put prizes in the fishpond. Then they asked people to pay money to fish for the prizes. My dad and I could run a fishpond."

Everyone cheered for Tommy's idea, even Margaret. No more ideas came, so Mrs. Howard left.

At the end of the day, Mr. Joliet said, "Now will each of you think about what you could do to make money at the carnival."

That evening, Margaret thought and thought about what she could do.

The next morning she told Mr. Joliet her idea.

Mr. Joliet gave Margaret space to work in at the back of the room. In her space, Margaret started placing dominoes on end. She placed each domino very carefully. She left a space between each one.

She had to be so very, very careful. If even one domino fell, it would fall on the domino next to it, and one by one all the dominoes would fall down. Margaret worked hard. She made all kinds of lines and curves.

Just about everyone watched as Margaret worked on her balancing act of lines and curves.

Margaret never saw who let the pencil fall between one of the long curves.

"I can't get it out," she said. "If I hit just *one* domino, they will all fall down."

"I'll get it for you," said Tommy.

Mr. Joliet caught Tommy's arm just in time and held him back.

"I will do it, Tommy," he said.

Very carefully, Mr. Joliet pulled out the pencil.

The next day Margaret finished balancing the last domino. Everyone wanted to be the one to push down the first domino. Even Tommy asked to be the one.

Margaret said, "The name of the one to do that will be pulled out of a box, and you will have to pay to get your name in that box."

Mr. Joliet said, "The name will be pulled from a box on the night of the carnival."

Everyone cheered. Margaret was very happy. She was so happy she forgot to watch where her foot was. As she started to leave, her foot hit the end domino.

Click, click, click, click, click, click! The dominoes started to fall one after the other. Ten dominoes fell down and then they stopped! Margaret had left too big a space.

Carefully . . . very, very, very carefully, she placed the fallen dominoes back up. This time she left just the right space between them.

On the day of the carnival when Margaret went to fish for a prize from the fishpond, she saw Tommy. He was watching people go up to his fishpond.

Margaret asked, "Why aren't you working, Tommy?"

"My father has too much help," he said. "He must have ten people helping him. Even my big brother is helping."

"Oh," said Margaret. She fished in the pond anyway. She caught a little plastic frog.

She was on her way to show it to Tommy, when Mrs. Howard said it was time for the *Domino Push.*

Mrs. Howard waited for everyone to gather at the back of the room.

Then Margaret let the oldest person in the room draw the name from the box. It was Jean's great-grandmother.

Jean's great-grandmother put on her glasses. Then she read,

Tommy pushed to the front of the crowd. Then he just stopped and looked at Margaret.

"Well, push," said Margaret.

Tommy pushed harder than was needed, but still it went wonderfully. *Click, click, click,* a hundred times *click,* one by one the dominoes fell.

When the last domino had fallen, a big cheer went up! Tommy looked right at Margaret and said, "There! I pushed down something that you balanced, and this time you wanted me to push it down."

"Yes," said Margaret. "I did want you to push it down. My *Domino Push* made the most money at this carnival."

Right then a big cheer went up for the balancing girl. And Margaret was sure she heard Tommy join in with the big cheer.

Story Wrap-up

Summary Questions

At first, Tommy did not think much of Margaret's balancing skill. These questions will help you tell what changed his mind.

1. What were some ways that Margaret showed her special skill?
2. Why do you think Tommy never showed Margaret how good he was at balancing things?
3. How did Margaret use her skill at the school carnival?
4. How do you think Tommy felt when his name was pulled for the Domino Push? Tell why.
5. Do you think Margaret and Tommy will become friends after the carnival? Tell why or why not.

The Reading and Writing Connection

Think about the things the children in Margaret's room did at the school carnival. Did you like those ideas?

What ideas do you have for a school carnival? Some examples might be using a special skill or playing a favorite game.

Write about some things the children in your room might do at a school carnival. Try to use some of the words in the box.

carnival	**oldest**	**balancing**
plastic	**careful**	**dominoes**
pay	**tower**	**principal**

Castles

by Marci Ridlon

Bricks stacked up
from a
torn down building
make
a castle
thick and strong.

Empty cans
can do
for towers
if you stack them
low
and long.

Reading in Science: Textbook

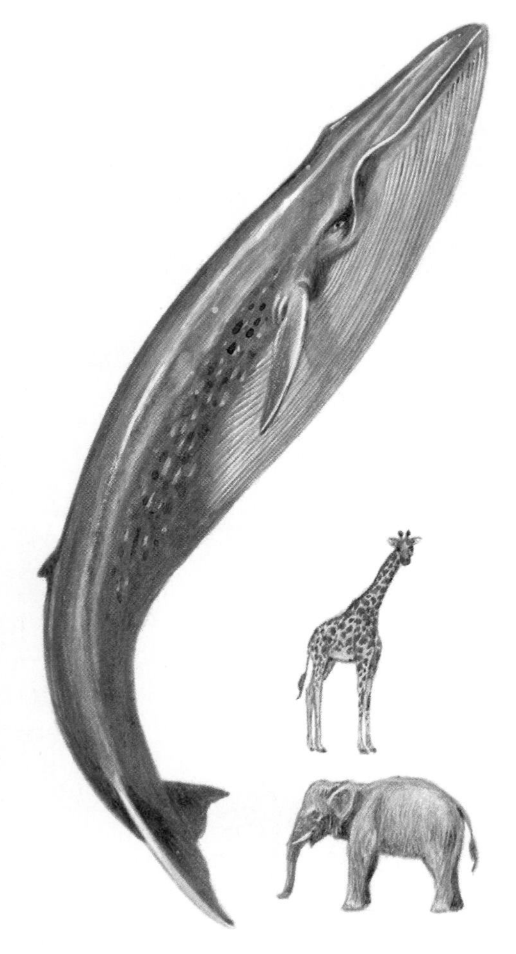

HOW BIG IS BIG?

Animals live in all parts of the world. They come in many sizes. Some animals are so tiny that you can't see them. Some are so huge that it's hard to even picture them in your mind. Find out just how big some animals are.

Do you know which animal is the tallest of all? It is the **giraffe.** A giraffe is taller than any other animal on land. It is about as tall as three grown-up people. The giraffe has a very long neck and very long legs.

A giraffe is so tall that it can see things that are a long way off. If it sees something frightening, the giraffe has time to run away. The giraffe's long legs help it run very fast.

The giraffe is the tallest animal on land, but the **elephant** is the biggest. An elephant can weigh as much as sixty grown-up people!

Elephants live in **herds**. A herd is a group of animals that live together. They care for each other and look for food together.

In some herds there are only four or five elephants, but in other herds there may be up to a thousand elephants!

Not all big animals live on land. Some live in the water. The **whale shark** is a very big fish. It is longer than four cars. It weighs as much as two elephants.

Many people are afraid of sharks, but no one needs to be afraid of the whale shark. The whale shark is quite gentle and eats only small plants and fish.

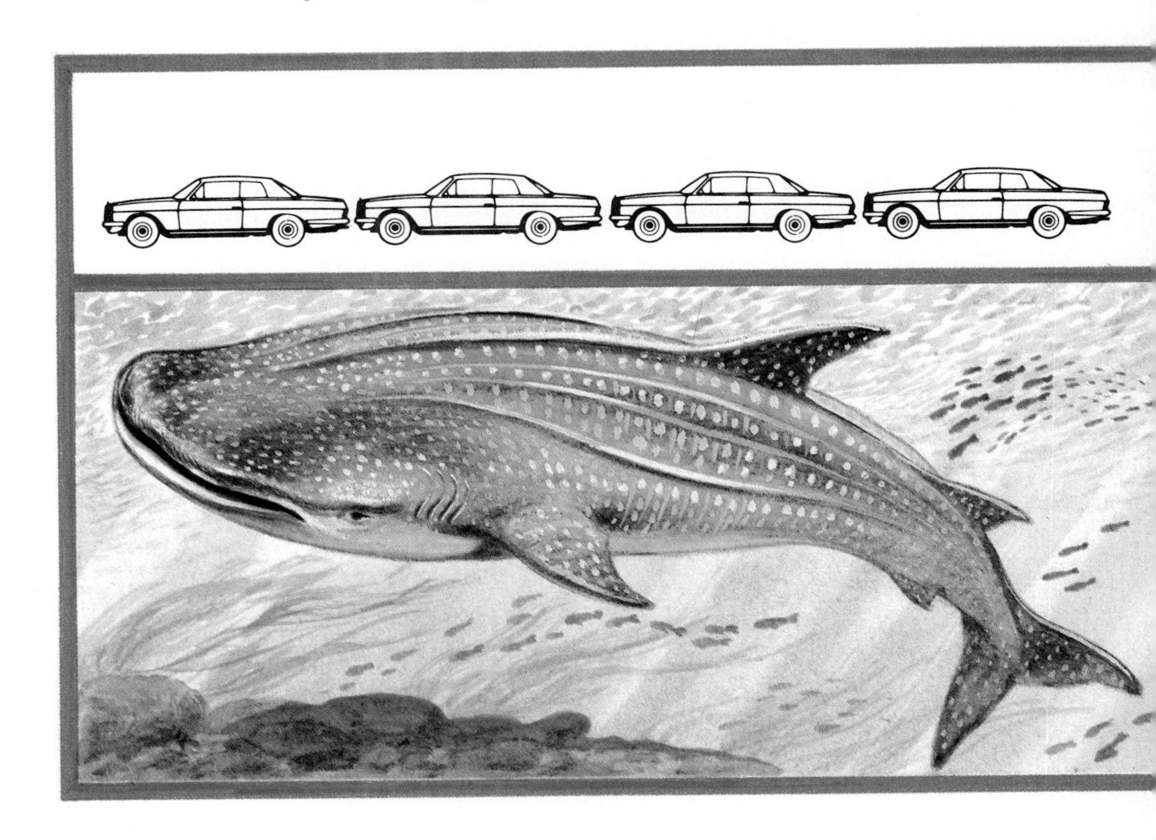

The biggest animal that has ever lived on land *or* sea is the **blue whale.** The blue whale is huge. It weighs more than one thousand grown-up people. It is longer than seven cars!

Whales live in the sea but they must come to the top of the water to breathe. The whale's nose is on the top of its head.

Selection Wrap-up

Summary Questions

1. What is the tallest animal on land?
2. What is the biggest animal on land?
3. What is the biggest animal that has ever lived on land or in the sea?

Pictograph Activity

Use drawings of cars to make a pictograph that shows the size of the whale shark and the blue whale.

Remember, a whale shark is as long as four cars and a blue whale is as long as seven cars.

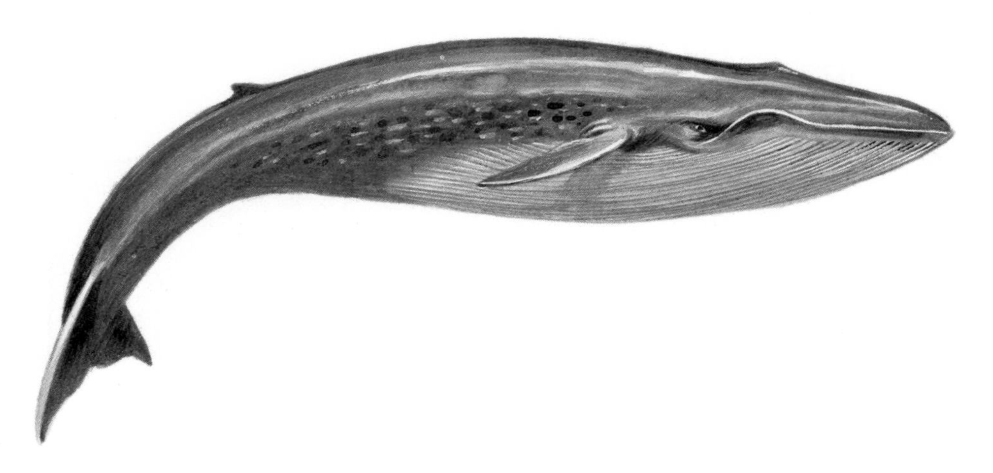

Vocabulary

A Better Word

It's fun to tell your friends about something you've done or something you've seen. When you do, you should use words that will make it easy to understand exactly what you mean.

Sometimes one word instead of another will make the meaning of what you are saying clearer.

Suppose you wanted to tell someone about the size of a whale. You could say a whale is *big,* or you could say a whale is *huge.*

The words *big* and *huge* mean about the same thing, but the word *huge* makes the size of the whale clearer.

The two words in heavy black letters in each pair of sentences below have almost the same meaning. Read the sentences. Decide which sentence makes the meaning of the picture clearer.

1. Paddy thinks this is a **good** dinner.
2. Paddy thinks this is a **wonderful** dinner.

Which of these sentences more clearly tells about the picture? Why?

3. Bippy caught a **tiny** fish.
4. Bippy caught a **little** fish.

Which of these sentences more clearly tells about the picture? Why?

A Thousand Pails of Water

by Ronald Roy

Yukio lives in a small village in Japan. One day he finds a whale stuck between some rocks. Can Yukio help the whale?

Yukio lived in a village where people fished to make their living.

One day Yukio walked down to the sea. As he walked by the edge of the water, he saw a whale. The whale was stuck between some rocks.

Yukio knew that the whale would not live long out of the sea.

"I will help you," he said to the whale. But how? The whale was huge.

Yukio raced to the water's edge. Was the tide coming in or going out?

It was coming in, he decided.

Yukio filled his pail with water and threw it over the head of the huge whale.

"You are so big and my pail is so small," he cried, "but I promise I will carry a thousand pails of water if I must, to save you."

Yukio filled his pail once more. The second pail went on the head as well, and then another and another. Yukio knew he must wet all of the whale or it would die in the sun.

Yukio went to the sea many times. He threw water on the whale's body. Then he threw water on the tail, and then on the head.

Yukio walked to the other side of the huge whale. He was so tired, he sat down. Then he looked at the whale and remembered his promise.

Yukio went back to the sea to fill his pail. How many had he filled? He had lost count, but he knew he must not stop.

Yukio fell, and the very important water ran from his pail. He cried and cried.

Then a wave touched his foot as if to say, "Get up and carry more water. I am coming, but I am very slow."

Yukio filled his pail over and over. His back hurt, and his arms hurt – but still he threw more water on the whale.

Once more he fell, but this time he did not get up.

Yukio could feel himself being lifted.

"You have worked hard, little one," said his grandfather. "Now let us help."

Yukio watched his grandfather throw his first pail of water and go for another.

"Faster!" Yukio wanted to shout, for his grandfather was old and walked slowly.

Then Yukio heard the sound of others. His father and the village people were running toward the sea. They were carrying pails and anything else that would hold water.

Some of the villagers took off their shirts and wet them in the sea. These they placed on the whale's body. Soon the whale was wet all over.

The village people carried water from the sea to the whale many times. Slowly the sea came closer and closer. At last it covered the whale's huge tail. Yukio knew the whale would be saved.

Yukio's father came and sat by him. "Thank you, Father," Yukio said, "for asking the village people to help."

"You are good and you have worked very hard," his father said, "but to save a whale, many hands must carry the water."

Now the huge whale was moving with each new wave. Suddenly a great wave lifted him from the rocks. He was still for just a second, then he swam out to sea.

The villagers watched, as the whale swam farther and farther into the water. Then they turned and walked toward the village.

Yukio, who was asleep, was carried by his father. Yukio had carried a thousand pails of water, and he was tired.

Story Wrap-up

Summary Questions

These questions will help you tell what happened when Yukio made a promise to the whale.

1. What was Yukio's promise? Why do you think he made this promise?
2. What did Yukio try to do to keep his promise?
3. Was Yukio really able to carry a thousand pails of water? Why not?
4. Why did the villagers help Yukio?
5. Pretend you are Yukio's grandfather. Tell Yukio's grandmother what happened.

The Reading and Writing Connection

What will happen if Yukio finds another whale stuck between two rocks? Will Yukio do things the same way as he did before? What might Yukio do in a different way?

Write what you think Yukio would do. The words in the box can help you.

promise	**touched**	**village**
pails	**edge**	**grandfather**
tide	**stuck**	**covered**

UNTIL I SAW THE SEA

by Lilian Moore

Until I saw the sea
I did not know
that wind
could wrinkle water so.

I never knew
that sun
could splinter
a whole sea of blue.

Nor
did I know before,
a sea breathes in and out
upon a shore.

Poinsettia and Her Family

by Felicia Bond

Poinsettia thinks that there is too much family in her house. How will she feel when she has the house all to herself?

Poinsettia had six brothers and sisters, a mother, and a father.

They lived in a fine, old house that had plants and flowers all around it.

Outside, there were big plants in which to hide and a rock out front to sit on.

Inside, there was a window seat for reading. It was red. There was a lovely bathroom. It was blue. Poinsettia thought it was a wonderful house.

One day Poinsettia came home from the library with a book about a dancing rabbit.

She walked by her mother in the garden and her father in the kitchen, and headed for the red leather window seat.

If the sun were coming in the window just right, it would spread like warm butter over her book. Poinsettia walked faster.

The sun was coming in the window just right. *But* it was spreading like warm butter over the body of little Julius who was asleep on the red leather window seat.

"I will go outside and sit on the rock," Poinsettia said angrily.

But the rock could hardly be seen for all of Poinsettia's brothers and sisters sitting on it.

Poinsettia stomped off toward the lovely blue bathroom. The tub would be just right for reading. But there in the tub was Chick Pea.

"This house would be great if it were not for one thing," Poinsettia said angrily. "There are too many of us in it! I cannot go anywhere without running into a brother or a sister, a mother or a father!"

The next day, Poinsettia's father and mother told the family that they were moving. "We will look for a new house," they said. "This one is too small for us."

"Oh, no, it's not," Poinsettia thought. "It's the family that's too big." Poinsettia didn't say anything, but she decided right then and there that she would not go with them.

When the family left, Poinsettia hid in the plants. No one saw her.

She hid there in the plants for a long time, just in case they came back. They didn't.

"Good!" Poinsettia said, and holding her book close to her, ran to the red leather window seat.

The light had never been more buttery. The leather had never been as warm. Poinsettia sat in the red leather seat and read two pages.

Then she ran outside to the rock. The rock had never felt so good.

Poinsettia read three more pages. But now the wind was blowing, and it was even starting to snow.

Poinsettia ran inside.

She warmed herself in a lovely hot bath. She read six more pages. Then she stopped and looked at the lovely blue bathroom. It had never looked bluer.

"I am a very happy pig," she said.

Poinsettia let the water out of the tub.

As the snow came down harder, Poinsettia fell asleep. She dreamed about the dancing rabbit.

It snowed and snowed all day and into the evening. By the time it was dark, Poinsettia had read her book six times.

She pulled an old bedspread around her and looked for something to eat. What little food there was she ate.

"This house is not as it used to be," she said to herself.

"What I need is a rope! If I had a rope, I could tie the rope to two chairs and put the bedspread over it. Then I would have a house inside a house. What a good idea."

Poinsettia looked everywhere for some rope. All she found was some string.

But hidden under a bookcase in her bedroom, Poinsettia found a photograph.

It was an old photograph of her family. Poinsettia remembered taking it herself. This was too much for Poinsettia.

She carefully made a little hole in the top of the photograph. Through the hole she pulled the string she had found.

"This is all I have left of my family!" Poinsettia cried, and cried, and cried.

Then she heard, "Poinsettia! Poinsettia!" Poinsettia thought she was going to faint!

There were her six brothers and sisters, her mother and her father, all crowded together and all smiling.

"We would have been back sooner," Poinsettia's father said, "but the car got stuck in the snow. It's a good thing there are so many of us. We all got out and pushed."

"Pierre counted and said everyone was in the car. But he's only three and he doesn't count very well," said Petunia, the oldest.

"All the time we were away, Poinsettia," her mother said, "we talked about what a wonderful house this is. It is our home. Maybe we don't need as much room as we thought."

"Maybe not," Poinsettia said.

And shoulder to shoulder, all crowded together, they spent the rest of that night, and many other nights together

... as together as nine pigs could be

... in their fine, old house.

Story Wrap-up

Summary Questions

These questions will help you tell how Poinsettia's feelings changed.

1. What made Poinsettia's house so wonderful?
2. How did Poinsettia feel at first when she had the house to herself?
3. Tell what Poinsettia might have said to her family when they came home.

The Reading and Writing Connection

Poinsettia had many special places around her house. Write about the one you think was best. Try to use some of these words.

bathroom	**kitchen**	**bedroom**
window	**rock**	**leather**
seat	**tub**	**photograph**

Skill

Picture Maps

A map is a special drawing that shows what a part of the earth looks like. Maps can show different things. A map can show all of a city, or a map can show just a small part of a city.

The map below is a map of someone's neighborhood. This map could be used to find the way to many houses in this neighborhood.

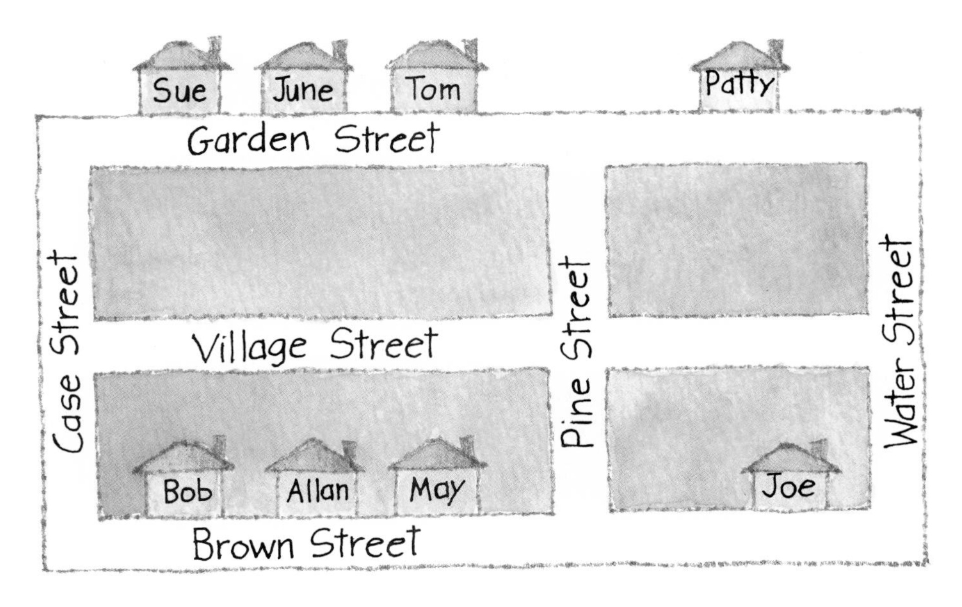

Some maps show things such as trees, rivers, houses, or libraries. On a map that shows many things, there is not enough space to show things exactly as they look. That is why many maps use small drawings called **symbols.**

Sometimes symbols look very much like the things they stand for. But sometimes a symbol will look nothing at all like the thing it stands for.

In order for the person using the map to know just what each symbol means, there must be a **key.** A key tells what each symbol stands for.

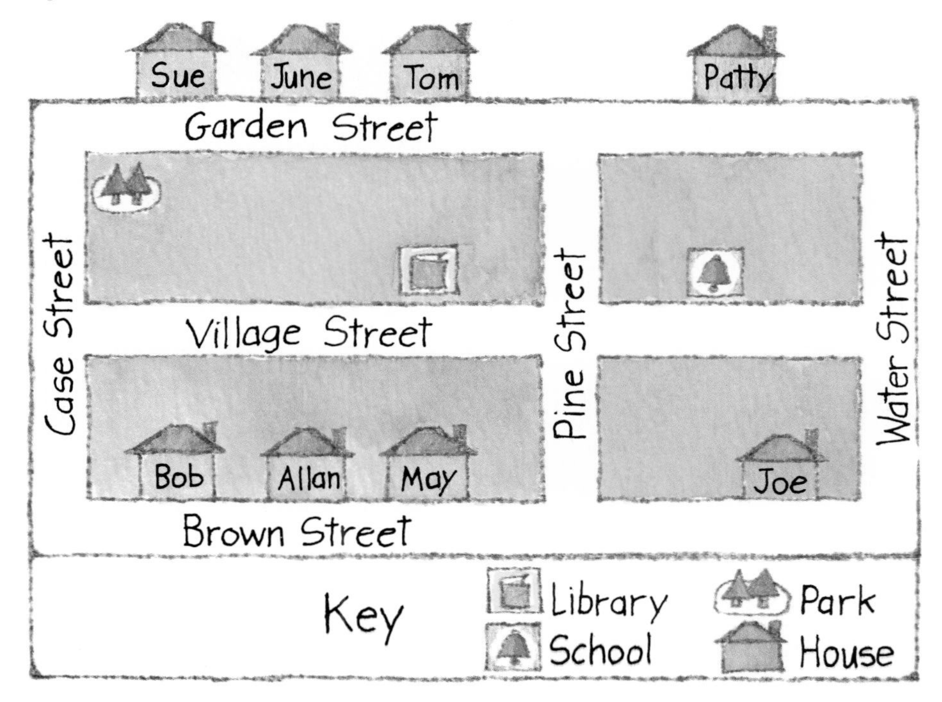

Some maps point out directions. These directions are shown by a drawing that has lines pointing to the letters N, S, E, and W. These letters stand for *north, south, east,* and *west.* The drawing is called a **compass rose.**

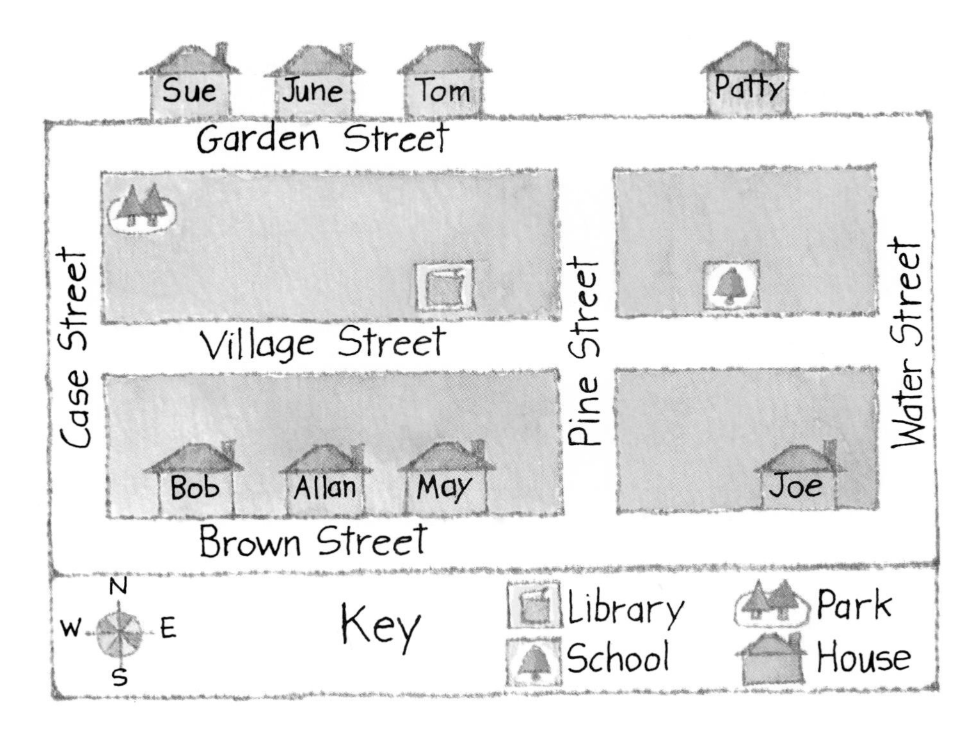

When reading a map, it is very important to know directions. If you are told to find the street that is east of the library, you must know which direction is east.

Think about what you have learned and then answer the questions below the map.

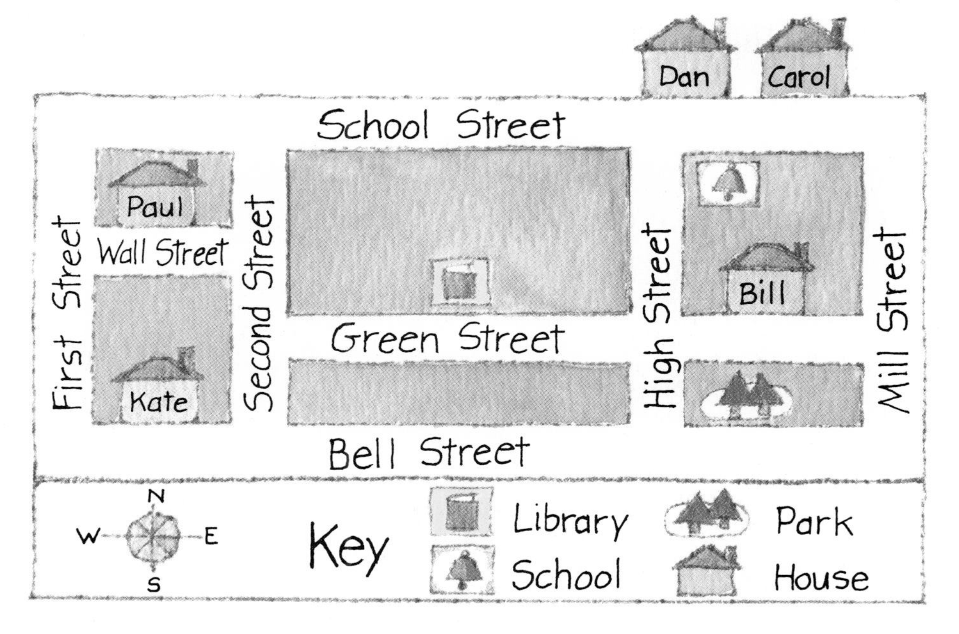

1. What streets would you use to go from Paul's house to the library?
2. On what street does Carol live?
3. Is the park north or south of the school?

Skill Summary

The next time you use a map, remember:
A key tells what each symbol stands for.
A compass rose shows directions.

The Case of the MISSING CODE BOOK

Bob Cox has just moved into a new house and he wants to make some new friends. Find out what he does.

The new boy stood by himself watching the children in the next yard play. He knew their names, but they didn't know his. He had just moved in.

There was a girl named Winnie and a girl named Hollie. There were two boys named Alex and John, and there was a dog named Panic.

The new boy watched the girl named Winnie take out a small brown book.

"We are here for a meeting," she said. "Secret Agents, it is time for us to learn a new code."

Then each Secret Agent took a turn looking through a small brown book.

The new boy wanted to see the book, too, but whenever he started to move from his yard, Panic barked.

When the children went into the house, they left the small brown book in the yard. The new boy went over and picked it up. He opened the book and looked inside.

The new boy smiled. He liked codes. Then he had an idea.

Soon Winnie, Alex, John, Hollie, and Panic came back to get the small brown book.

"I put it here, but now it's missing," said Winnie.

They looked all over, but all they found was a piece of paper with nothing on it.

"Do you think this paper means anything?" Hollie asked.

"There could be a message in secret writing on it," said Alex.

"Secret writing?" the others asked.

"Yes," said Alex. "The message could be a clue to our missing Code Book. The writing may be invisible."

"What does *invisible* mean?" asked Hollie.

"It means you can't see it," said Alex.

"If you can't see something, what good is it?" said Hollie.

"Well, you *can* see something, if you know how," said Alex.

"Then how?" asked Winnie, Hollie, and John.

"Come on. I'll show you," said Alex. He went inside the house and turned on the light.

"First, you hold the paper next to the light," he said. "If the person who left this message wrote it in milk, when we hold the paper next to the light, the writing will come out in brown letters."

Sure enough, there in front of them was a message. It said:

This is what John found under the rock.

"It's a picture map!" cried John. "Where should we go first?"

"Let's try the doghouse," said Winnie.
"Panic's bed is in his doghouse.
That's where the book must be."

Then everyone followed Winnie across
the yard to Panic's doghouse.

John stuck his head into the doghouse.
"There's nothing here," he said.

"Where should we go next?" asked Alex.

"There's a picture of a bed on the map,"
said Hollie. She thought for a second,
and then she said, "It must be *my* bed!
Sometimes Panic sleeps under my bed."

Hollie, Winnie, John, and Alex ran to the house. They looked under Hollie's bed. There was nothing there.

"What's next?" asked Hollie.

"Flowers," said Alex. "What could that mean?"

"It could mean the flower bed," said Winnie.

Out of the house they ran and sure enough, there was Panic digging away in the flower bed.

"Here's something," cried John, picking up a piece of paper.

As he opened it, they all looked. It said:

"Somebody is using our Code Book," shouted Winnie.

"They sure are!" said John.

"Let's try to read the message," said Alex. "I remember the code but we'd better write it out, or it will take all day."

Winnie took out a paper and wrote:

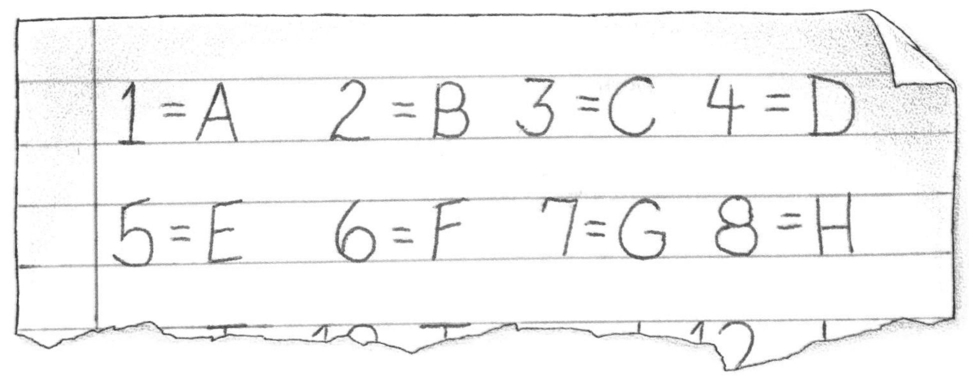

Then using the code, they wrote the message.

TO FIND
20-15 6-9-14-4

YOUR BOOK
25-15-21-18 2-15-15-11

TRY THE
20-18-25 20-8-5

PINE TREE
16-9-14-5 20-18-5-5

"The pine tree!" Hollie shouted and they all started across the yard.

There, stuck into a hole in the tree, was another paper.

"Here it is," shouted John.

"Read it," cried the others.

John opened the paper.

“What are those funny-looking letters?” asked Hollie.

“It could be a kind of mirror writing,” said Alex.

“What’s mirror writing?” asked Hollie.

“Get me a mirror and I’ll show you,” said Alex.

Hollie ran back to the house to get one.

“You put the mirror in front of the letters just like this,” said Alex.

Then they read:

"Who's Bob Cox?" asked Winnie.

Not one of them knew.

"I am!" the new boy shouted from his yard. "And here's your book." He held it out to Alex.

"You took our Code Book!" the others said.

"I thought we could have some fun," he said. "I was in a club before I moved here. I know lots of secret codes."

Winnie, Hollie, John, and Alex looked at each other.

"How'd you like to be a Secret Agent, Bob?" they all said together.

"Sure I would," said the new boy. "And you can have all my secrets for the Code Book!"

Story Wrap-up

Summary Questions

When Bob Cox moved into a new house, he wanted to make some new friends. These questions will help you tell how he tried to make friends.

1. What did Bob see and hear when he watched the children in the next yard?
2. What was Bob's idea?
3. Why did Bob want to send messages in code to the Secret Agents?
4. Pretend you belong to the Secret Agents' Club. Would you ask Bob to join? Tell why or why not.

The Reading and Writing Connection

Pretend you are Bob Cox. Write a message to a friend in your old neighborhood about the Secret Agents' Club. Try to use some of these words.

clue	**message**	**secret**
club	**mirror**	**invisible**
code	**meeting**	

Now write your message in code. Use the code in the Secret Agents' Book.

ALL ABOUT CODES

Would you like to send a secret message? Find out how codes are used to send secret messages.

A code is a special way of sending a message. People have been using codes for a long time. When a message is written in code, the one who writes the message must have a copy of the code. The one who reads the message must also have a copy of the code.

There are many different kinds of codes. The pages that follow tell about some codes.

One of the oldest codes is the letter code. This code uses one letter in place of another letter. To make a letter code, print the letters of the alphabet from A to Z. Then, next to each letter, print a different letter of the alphabet.

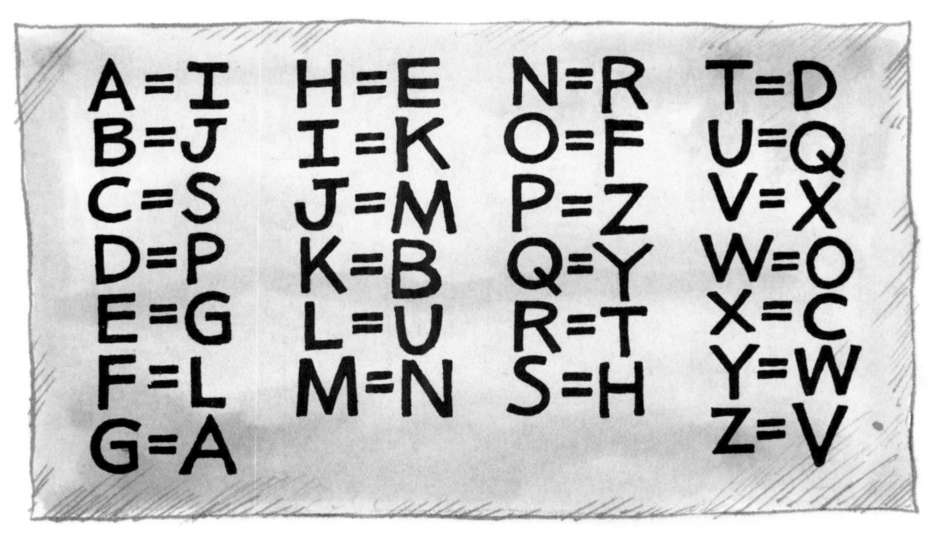

A=I	H=E	N=R	T=D
B=J	I=K	O=F	U=Q
C=S	J=M	P=Z	V=X
D=P	K=B	Q=Y	W=O
E=G	L=U	R=T	X=C
F=L	M=N	S=H	Y=W
G=A			Z=V

Can you read this message? Use the code to figure out what it says.

A picture code is another kind of code. In a picture code each picture stands for a different letter. All you have to do is think of a different picture for each letter of the alphabet.

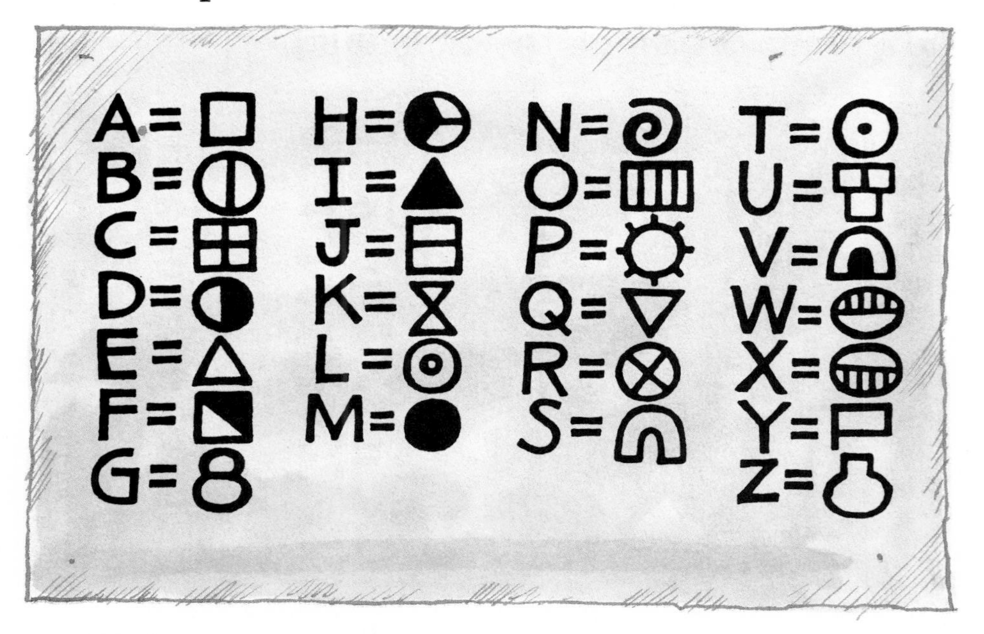

Using the picture code above, can you read this message?

In some codes a number is used in place of each letter.

A=26	H=19	N=13	T=7
B=25	I=18	O=12	U=6
C=24	J=17	P=11	V=5
D=23	K=16	Q=10	W=4
E=22	L=15	R=9	X=3
F=21	M=14	S=8	Y=2
G=20			Z=1

Can you read these messages?

14-22-22-7 14-22 26-7
7-19-22 15-18-25-9-26-9-2

25-9-18-13-20 2-12-6-9
24-12-23-22 25-12-12-16
4-18-7-19 2-12-6

Story Wrap-up

Summary Questions

These questions will help you tell what you learned about codes.

1. What is a code?
2. Why do people use codes?
3. Name the three codes you read about. Tell about each one.

The Reading and Writing Connection

Make your own code. Follow these directions.

1. Print the letters of the alphabet.
2. Next to each letter put a letter, number, or picture. This is your code.
3. Write a message in code.
4. Give a friend the message and a copy of the code.

Skill

Word Referents

You know that words such as *he*, *she*, *they*, *it*, *this*, and *that* don't mean much by themselves. You have to look at the words around such words to find out what these words mean.

Read this sentence.

Joe got tired of waiting, so **he** left.

In this sentence, the word *he* stands for the word Joe. The words *he* and *Joe* are in the same sentence.

What does the word in the heavy black letters in this sentence mean?

Sally was sleepy so **she** went to bed.

Sometimes one or more words in a sentence will stand for one or more words in another sentence. Read these sentences.

Don and Bob could not find Sue's book.
She forgot to tell **them** where to look.

In these sentences, the word *she* stands for the word *Sue*. The word *them* stands for the words *Don* and *Bob*.

The words *she* and *them* are in one sentence and the words they stand for are in another sentence.

What do the words in heavy black letters mean?

Father bought some eggs at the store.
He brought **them** home.

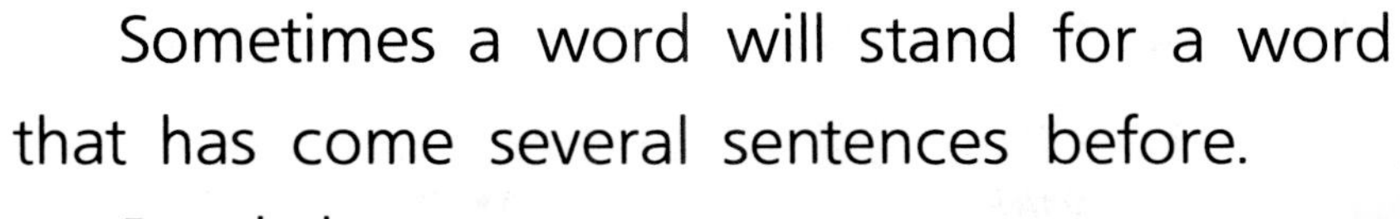

Sometimes a word will stand for a word that has come several sentences before.

Read these sentences.

The bird went out to find food. She found three seeds. She quickly ate one of them. Then she ate two more of them. **She** said, "**They** were very good."

In these sentences, the word *she* stands for the word *bird*, and the word *they* stands for the word *seeds*.

What do the words in heavy black letters in these sentences stand for?

Carla was on her way to school. She saw a red bird in a tree. She looked at its pretty color. She listened to its happy song. "I will draw a picture of **it** when I get to school," **she** thought.

Sometimes you have to think carefully about what *many* sentences are saying.

Read these sentences.

Mike said, "It is very nice **here.** I do not want to move to an apartment."

"You will like the apartment, Mike," said his mother.

"An apartment house will not be as nice as the house we live in now," said Mike.

If you think carefully about all the sentences, you will know that the word *here* means the house that Mike lives in now.

Now read these sentences. What do you think the word *here* means?

"Now that we're **here,** let's try to find a book we like," said Joan.

"We only have three dollars," said Jill.

"We can get a good book for three dollars in this bookstore," said Joan.

Skill Summary

Remember, when you come to words such as *he, she, they, it, this* and *that,* look at the words around such words to find out what they mean.

Treasure

The Rabbit and the Turnip

translated by Richard Sadler

illustrated by Carol Leeson

On a snowy winter morning, Little Rabbit finds two turnips. He leaves one of the turnips on the doorstep of his friend.

What happens to the turnip after that shows just how much Little Rabbit and his friends care about each other.

The Rabbit and the Turnip

Translated by Richard Sadler

Illustrated by Carol Leeson

It was a cold winter morning and snow covered the ground. Little Rabbit went out to look for food and he found two turnips. He gobbled up one of them. Then he said, "It is snowing so hard, and it is so cold that perhaps Little Donkey has nothing to eat. I will take my other turnip to him."

He ran to Little Donkey's house at once, but Little Donkey was out. So Little Rabbit left the turnip on Little Donkey's doorstep. Then he hopped back home.

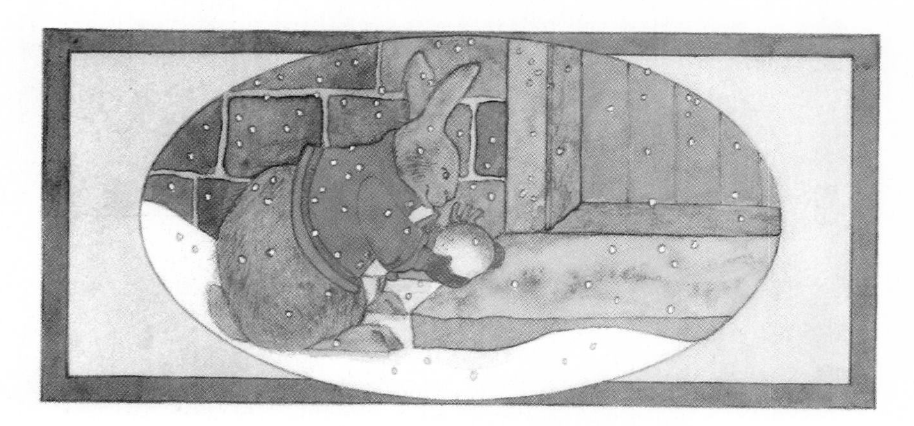

Now Little Donkey had also gone out to look for food and he had found a potato. When he got home and saw the turnip, he was very surprised. "Who could have put it there?" he thought.

Then Little Donkey said to himself, "It is snowing so hard, and it is so cold. Perhaps Little Sheep has nothing to eat. I will take it to her."

He rolled the turnip to Little Sheep's house. But there was no sign of Little Sheep. He left the turnip on Little Sheep's table. Then he ran back home.

In the meantime, Little Sheep had also been looking for food. She had found a cabbage. She was happily trotting home to eat it.

When Little Sheep got to her house and found the turnip, she was surprised. Who could have put it there? She decided to give the turnip to Little Deer.

It was snowing so hard, and it was so cold, Little Sheep felt sure Little Deer would be hungry.

So Little Sheep took the turnip to Little Deer's house, but there was no one at home. She left the turnip on Little Deer's window sill and off she went.

It so happened that Little Deer was also out looking for food and she found some nice green leaves. She, too, was very surprised to find the turnip waiting for her at home.

"I will give this beautiful turnip
to Little Rabbit," said Little Deer.
"It is snowing so hard, and it is so cold
perhaps he has nothing to eat."

Little Deer ran to Little Rabbit's house at once. And there was Little Rabbit, fast asleep. Little Deer did not want to wake him up, so she pushed the turnip inside the door and hurried away.

When Little Rabbit got up and found the turnip, he thought he must be dreaming.

Then he said to himself, "How nice of someone to give me this turnip!" And he gobbled it all up!

Story Wrap-up

Summary Questions

Think about what each animal did for a friend. These questions will help you.

1. What did Little Rabbit do to help Little Donkey? Why do you think he did this?
2. Where did Little Donkey take the turnip? What happened then?
3. Who ended up with the turnip? Why was this a good ending?
4. There was only one turnip to share, but it made four animals happy. How?

The Reading and Writing Connection

Imagine that you are Little Rabbit. You are about to bring the turnip to Little Donkey's house and you want Little Donkey to know who brought it.

Write a note telling Little Donkey about the turnip. Tell him why you are giving him the turnip, and be sure to sign the note! The words in the box can help you.

turnip	**perhaps**	**beautiful**
donkey	**gobble**	**hurried**

Magazine Wrap-up

What Did They Do?

Bob Cox, Yukio, Poinsettia, and Little Rabbit all had something they wanted to do.

Which characters wanted to do something for someone else? ... What did they do?

Which characters wanted to do something for themselves? ... What did they do?

Word Watch

Which words below name things that are alike in some way? In what way are the things named alike?

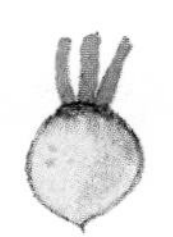

thousand
whale
turnip
hundred

leather
plastic
cabbage
giraffe

A New Neighbor

Suppose one of the characters you read about in Magazine Two could move into the house next to yours. Write some sentences telling which character you would like it to be. Tell why.

Books to Enjoy

Oink and Pearl by Kay Chorao

Two pigs show how a little brother and a big sister can get along together.

Grandma's Wheelchair by Lorraine Henriod

Thomas and Grandma and her wheelchair have many good times together.

Troll Country by Edward Marshall

A young girl meets a troll in the woods and proves that she is smarter than he is.

Adventures
Magazine Three

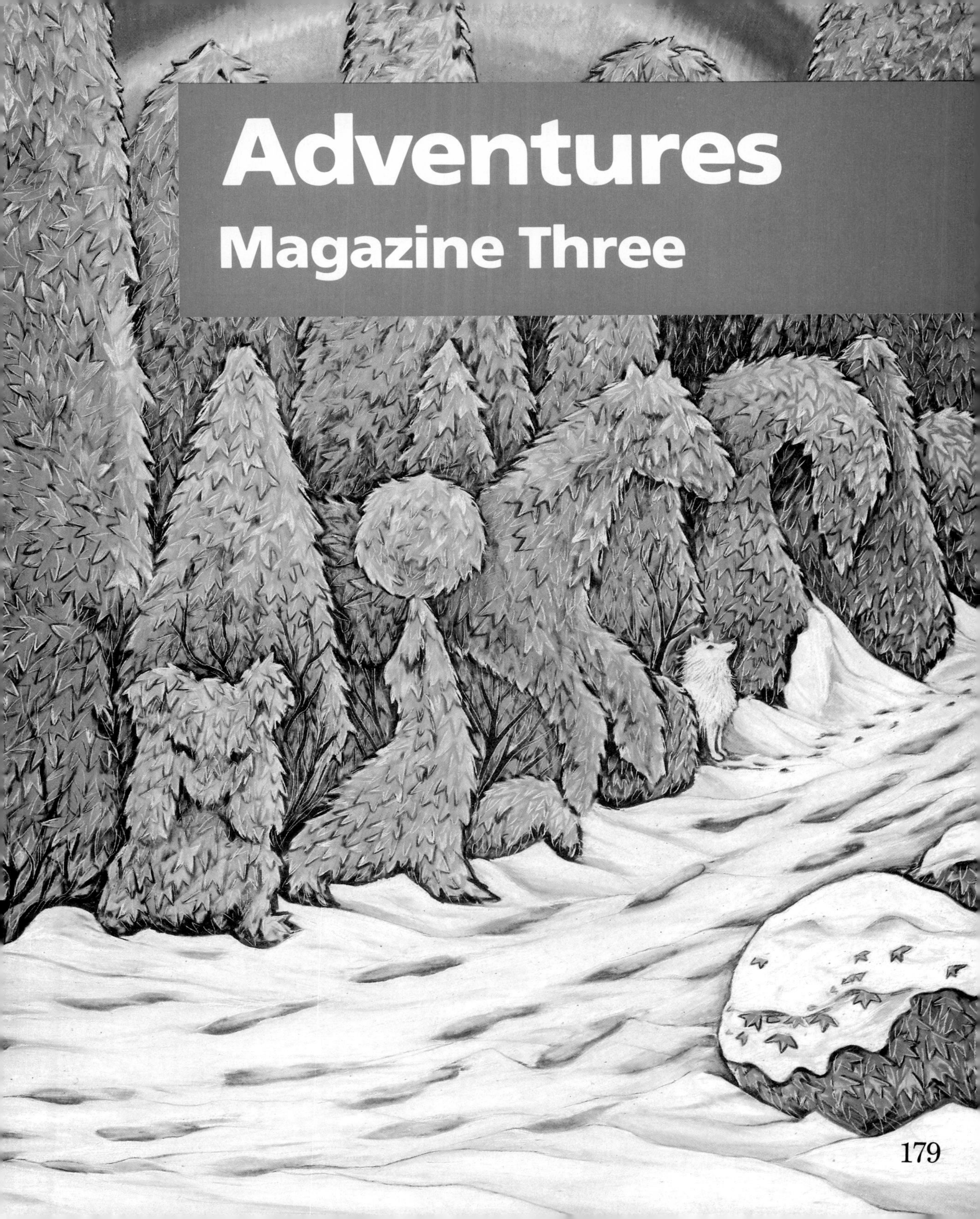

Contents

Stories

Play

Content Selection

Poems

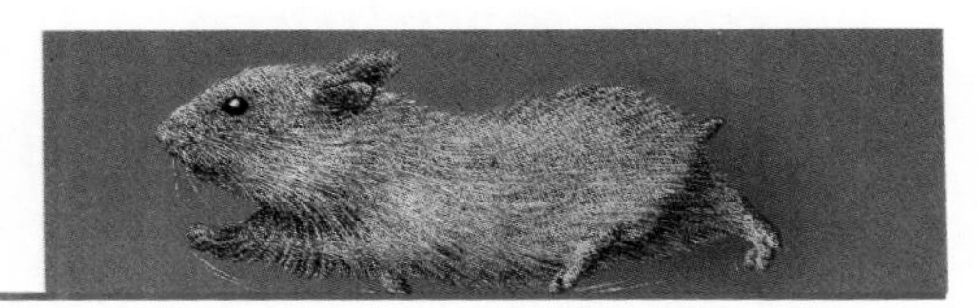

Skills

Vocabulary

JASPER and the Hero Business

by Betty Horvath

Jasper wants to be a hero, but first he must learn what a hero is. Find out what Jasper learns about heroes.

Jasper lived in a house on the corner. All day long people hurried by the house, first on their way to work and then on their way home.

Jasper didn't hurry. He didn't have any place to go. Sometimes he didn't have anything to do. He just sat under the tree and watched all the people hurry by.

Sometimes they stopped and talked to him. Sometimes they asked him questions.

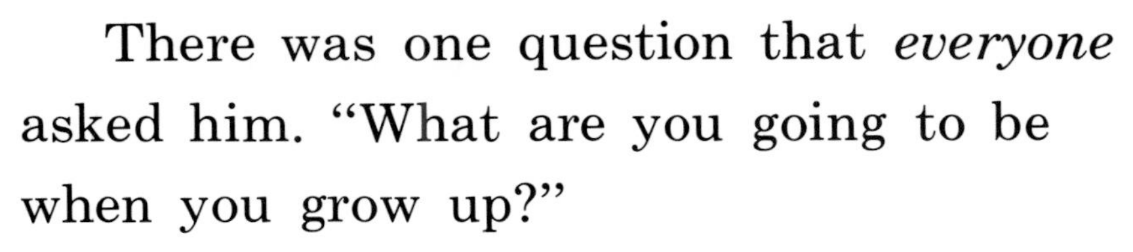

There was one question that *everyone* asked him. "What are you going to be when you grow up?"

"I'm going to be a hero," Jasper said. And then they laughed.

"Wait and see," thought Jasper. "Someday I'm going to be a big hero. I will have my picture in the paper."

"Okay, Jasper the hero," said his sister Paula, "I have a job for you." She handed Jasper a rake.

"This is no job for a hero," said Jasper. He raked up the leaves anyway.

Then he went back to sit under his tree and wait for something brave to do.

Just then, a fire engine went racing by.

"There go some heroes," said Jasper. "They're off to help people in trouble."

That night in the newspaper, there was a picture of a firefighter. He was helping a boy from a window. Jasper cut the picture out of the paper.

That's the way his hero board started.

Every time Jasper read about someone brave, he pinned the story to the board.

"Someday," said Jasper, "my picture will be up there, too."

"I'm sure it will," said his mother.

Jasper decided to take his dog Rover for a walk. When they turned the corner, Jasper saw a man running toward him.

"Maybe this is a thief coming!" Jasper thought. "When he gets closer, Rover and I can catch him."

When the man got closer, Jasper saw that it was just Mr. Brown out for his morning run.

"I'm never going to be a hero," thought Jasper. He turned the corner. There on the ground was a piece of paper. It was money!

"If I can't be brave," said Jasper, "it will be good to have money."

When they got to the next corner, Jasper heard the sound of crying. "Maybe someone is in trouble," thought Jasper, "maybe even in danger! Now I may get to be a hero."

Then he saw who was crying. It was a little boy. He was standing in front of Jasper's house.

"Are you lost?" Jasper asked. "Can I take you home?"

Jasper could see it now. The headlines in the paper would say:

HERO TAKES LOST BOY HOME

"I'm not lost," said the little boy. "My money's lost."

"Oh," said Jasper. "I just found some money. It must be yours."

The little boy took the money. He didn't say anything. He just watched Jasper and Rover go into the house.

"Maybe I'm not going about this hero business in the right way," thought Jasper.

"Do you know any heroes?" he asked his mother.

"Look out the window," said his mother. "There is a hero coming up the walk now."

Jasper ran to the window.

"That's Father coming up the walk," he said. "I never knew he was a hero."

"There are all kinds of heroes," said his mother. "Your father worked hard today to make money to pay the bills. I think he's a hero."

"Then I will put his picture on my board," said Jasper.

So Jasper found a picture of his father and pinned it on the board. Then he thought, "Mother works hard, so she must be a hero, too." He pinned a picture of his mother next to the picture of his father.

But there was still the empty space for *his* picture. He was getting older every second, and he still wasn't a hero.

While Jasper and his family were eating supper, someone came to the door. Jasper's father went to see who was there. When he came back, he was carrying a bunch of flowers.

"Jasper, these are for you," he said. "A little boy left them. He said you gave him some money."

"Oh, *him*." said Jasper. "I found some money, but it was his. I just gave it back to him."

At first no one said anything. Then Paula said, "I'm sure that little boy thinks Jasper is a hero."

"Who, me? A hero?" asked Jasper.

"Sure," said Paula, "If someone *thinks* you're a hero, you are one. It's time to pin your picture on the hero board."

Paula helped Jasper pin the picture on the board. Under it they wrote, "Jasper the Hero." The board was finished now. There was no more empty space.

"Now that you are a hero," said Paula, "what are you going to be next?"

"You don't ever stop being a hero," said Jasper. "But now that I am a hero, I think I'll work on being a doctor. What are you going to do?"

"Me?" asked Paula. "I'm going to try very hard not to get sick!"

Story Wrap-up

Summary Questions

These questions will help you tell how Jasper learned about different kinds of heroes.

1. Which pictures did Jasper put on his hero board at first? Why did he pick them?
2. Why did Jasper put pictures of his mother and father on his hero board?
3. What did Jasper learn about being a hero? Was Jasper a hero? Why or why not?

The Reading and Writing Connection

Can you add to Jasper's hero board? About whom would you write? Tell why this person is a hero. Try to use some of these words.

brave	**hero**	**business**
doctor	**danger**	**firefighter**

Skill

Common Syllables

You know that a syllable is a part of a word that can be said alone. You also know that some syllables are used in words so often they are called **common syllables.**

In the sentences below, you will see two common syllables you already know. Read the sentences.

1. Be **careful** when you cross the street.
2. There was a **lovely** flower in the garden.

Look at the words in heavy black letters. The word *careful* ends with the common syllable *ful*. The word *lovely* ends with the common syllable *ly*. The common syllables *ful* and *ly* are often found at the ends of words.

Sometimes other common syllables are added to the beginnings of words. Read the sentences below.

1. Sue put the paper **beside** the pencil.
2. Tom is going to **exchange** his blue shirt for a red one.

Each of the words in heavy black letters begins with a common syllable. In the first sentence, the word *beside* begins with the common syllable *be*.

In the second sentence, the word *exchange* begins with the common syllable *ex*. The letters *be* and *ex* are common syllables that are found at the beginnings of many words.

Sometimes when the letters *be* come at the beginning of a word, they are *not* a common syllable. For example, in the word *better,* the letters *be* are only a part of the first syllable *bet*. The letters *be* are not a common syllable in the word *best* because the word *best* has only one syllable.

But often when you see the letters *be* at the beginning of a word, they will be a common syllable that stands for the sounds you hear at the beginning of *beside*.

When the letters *ex* come at the beginning of a word, they are always a common syllable and most of the time they will stand for the sounds you hear at the beginning of the word *exchange*.

Now let's see if you can use what you know about the sounds for the common syllables *be* and *ex* to read some words that begin with those syllables.

1. The sign over the door said: **EXIT.**
2. Pat will be here every day **except** Monday.
3. The sign said: **Beware** of the dog.
4. We could see the big fish just **beneath** the top of the water.

Skill Summary

Remember, when a new word begins with the letters *be*, try the sounds for the common syllable *be* in the word *beside*. When a new word begins with the common syllable *ex*, try the sounds for the common syllable in *exchange*.

The Shoemakers and the Elves

Martha and Peter are shoemakers, but all they have left is enough leather to make one pair of shoes. What will happen to them now?

In the Play

Storyteller	Martha	Peter
Gentleman	Alice	Woman
	Elves	

Storyteller: Peter and Martha spent their days making shoes. They worked very hard, and they were good shoemakers. Still, they had trouble making enough money to live on. It seemed that the harder they worked, the poorer they got. Finally, all they had left was one piece of leather.

Peter: Martha, this is a sad day for us. We have enough leather to make only one more pair of shoes.

Martha: Let's not talk about it tonight. We will make the shoes in the morning, and then we'll decide what to do next.

Storyteller: So Peter and Martha left the piece of leather on their worktable and went off to bed. The next morning when they went into their shop, they found a big surprise.

Peter: Martha, am I dreaming or do you see a pair of shoes on the table?

Martha: You are not dreaming. I see the shoes, too. Where could they have come from?

Peter: I don't know, but they seem to be very well made. We should be able to get a good price for them.

Martha: Here comes someone now.

(Man enters shop.)

Peter: Come in, sir. How may I help you?

Man: I have come to buy a pair of shoes.

Peter: How about this pair of shoes, sir?

Man: They are quite beautiful.

Peter: They are very well made, too.

Man: I will take them. Here are four coins. That should be enough to pay for this nice pair of shoes. Good day.

Martha: Good day to you, sir.

(Man leaves shop.)

Peter: Martha, he gave me *four* coins! Never before have we made so much money on just one pair of shoes.

Martha: Now we have enough money to buy leather for *two* pairs of shoes!

Storyteller: That afternoon, Peter and Martha went shopping for leather. They were so tired when they got home that they decided to wait until morning to make the shoes. They left the leather on their worktable.

Storyteller: The next morning when they went into their shop, they were again surprised!

Peter: Martha, it's happened again! Someone took the leather we left and made *two* pairs of shoes.

Martha: These shoes are even more beautiful than the others. Who could be doing this?

Peter: I don't know, but here come two people now. Perhaps we can sell one pair of the shoes to them.

(Woman and daughter enter shop.)

Martha: May I help you?

Woman: Yes, I have come for a pair of shoes for my daughter Alice.

Alice: Mama, look at those shoes on the table! They are exactly what I want. They are so beautiful.

Peter: They are very well made.

Alice: I can't decide which pair I like best . . . the blue ones or the red ones.

Woman: Then we shall buy the blue ones *and* the red ones! Here . . . I think these coins will be enough to cover the price of the shoes. Come on Alice, we must go.

Martha: Good day and do come again.

(Woman and daughter leave.)

Peter: Martha, she gave me *eight* coins! Now we have enough money to buy leather to make *four* pairs of shoes.

Storyteller: On and on it went. Every night Peter and Martha would leave leather on the worktable. The next morning, they would find beautiful shoes that they would sell for a good price. Soon Peter and Martha had become quite rich. Many times they would slip into their shop late at night hoping to see who was making the shoes. No one was ever there.

Peter: Martha, we must find out who has been making these shoes for us.

Martha: I have been thinking about that too, and I have an idea. We can stay in the shop all night. Then we will see who comes to do our work for us.

Storyteller: So that night, Peter and Martha hid behind a chair in their shop and waited to see what would happen. Soon after midnight, four tiny elves came through the door and went right to work. As they worked, they said these words:

Elves: *We know what to do,*
And there's no time to lose.
With this piece of leather,
We'll make the best shoes ever.

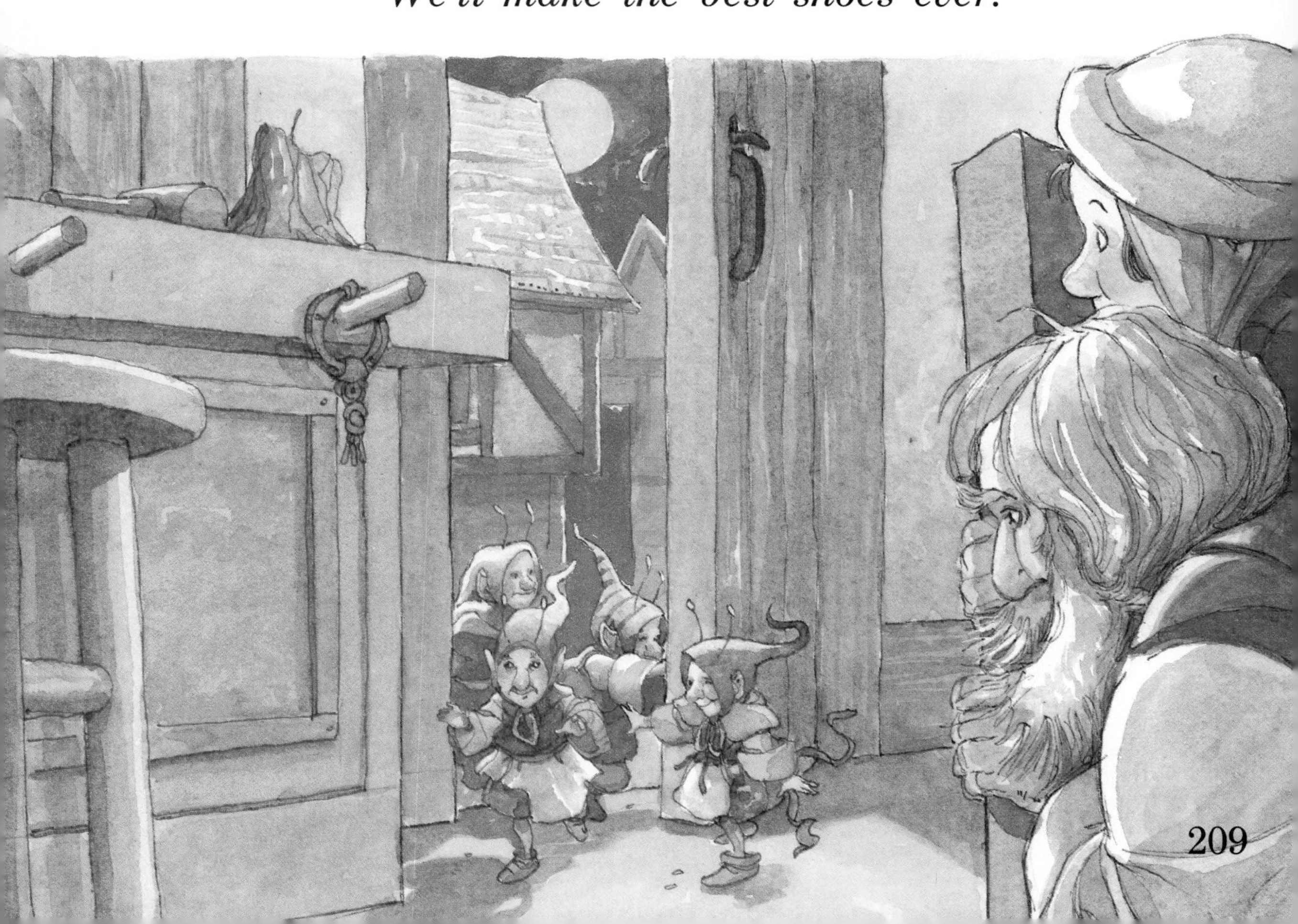

Storyteller: The four little elves pounded and sewed throughout the night. When the shoes were finished, they said these words:

Elves: *We've cut and sewed,*
And pounded and glued.
The shoes are made,
And now we're through.

Storyteller: Then just as quickly as the elves had come, they left! The next morning, Martha and Peter sat down to talk about what they had seen.

Martha: Those little elves have been doing all our work for us, and they have made us very rich. We must do something for them.

Peter: You are right, Martha, but what can we do?

Martha: It is very cold outside. I'm going to make each of them a little coat and a little hat.

Peter: I will make each of them a little pair of shoes.

Storyteller: Martha and Peter worked all day making the coats and hats and shoes. That night, they left the little coats and hats and shoes on the worktable. Then they hid behind the chair, just as they had done the night before. Soon after midnight, the elves came through the door. When they saw the coats and hats and shoes on the table, they put the things on and danced all around the room. As they danced, they said these words:

Elves: *Even though the cold winds blow,*
No more problems will we know.
There's nothing more to do or say,
So we'll be on our happy way.

Storyteller: Then the elves danced out the door. Martha and Peter never saw them again. From that time on, everything went well for the shoemakers.

Story Wrap-up

Summary Questions

Peter and Martha got some special help with their business. These questions will help you tell how and why they were helped.

1. How did the lives of the shoemakers change after the elves came?
2. Why do you think the elves picked Peter and Martha to help?

3. Do you think that Peter and Martha found a good way to help the elves? Tell why.

The Reading and Writing Connection

"The Shoemakers and the Elves" was written as a play. Pretend you are a newspaper reporter who writes about plays. You saw the play yesterday and you have to write about it.

Tell your readers what the play was about and why you did or did not like it. Try to use some of the words in the box.

elves	**sewed**	**poor**	**coins**

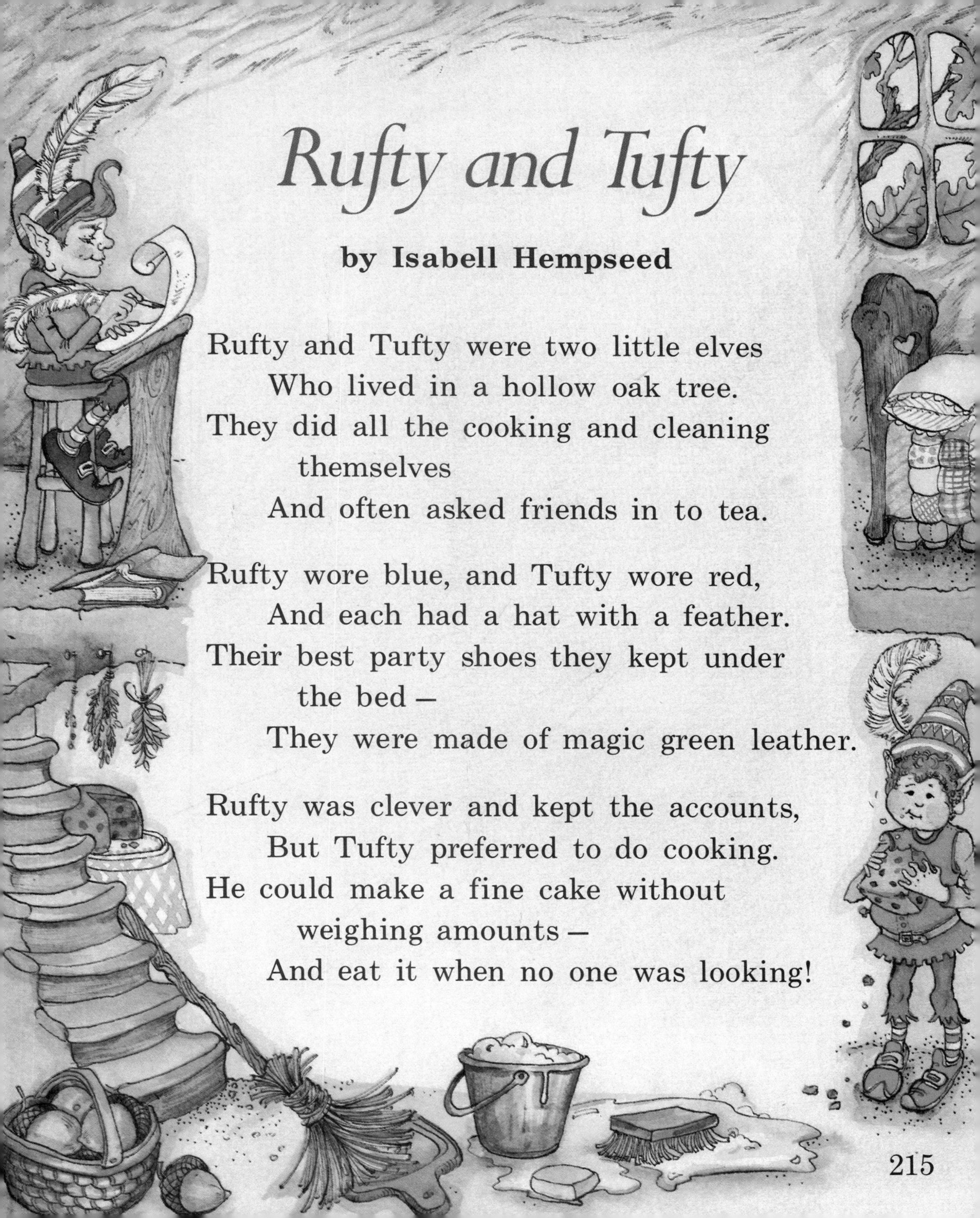

Rufty and Tufty

by Isabell Hempseed

Rufty and Tufty were two little elves
Who lived in a hollow oak tree.
They did all the cooking and cleaning themselves
And often asked friends in to tea.

Rufty wore blue, and Tufty wore red,
And each had a hat with a feather.
Their best party shoes they kept under the bed –
They were made of magic green leather.

Rufty was clever and kept the accounts,
But Tufty preferred to do cooking.
He could make a fine cake without weighing amounts –
And eat it when no one was looking!

Penelope Gets Wheels

by Esther Allen Peterson

Penelope wants some wheels. What kind of wheels does she want? What kind of wheels does she get?

It was Penelope's birthday. She got ten one-dollar bills.

"I am rich, and I am older now," she said to her mom. "I don't need to walk anymore. I will go on wheels."

"Wheels?" asked her mom.

"Yes," said Penelope. "I would like a car, but I know I'm not rich enough or old enough. I think I will buy a bicycle."

"You'll need a lot of money to buy a bicycle," said her mom.

"Ten dollars *is* a lot of money," Penelope said. Then she ran outside and down the street to the sports shop on the corner.

"Today is my birthday," she said to the salesperson. "I would like to buy that blue racing bike. How much does it cost?"

"This bicycle costs one hundred dollars," the salesperson said.

Penelope pointed to another bike. "How much is that one?"

"Ninety dollars," said the salesperson.

"I'm not that rich," Penelope said.

Penelope looked at many things. But she didn't want to buy anything she saw.

Then she saw some roller skates. They cost nine dollars.

She picked up a skate and spun its wheels. "I guess these are all I have enough to buy," she said.

Penelope paid for the skates.

She went outside, put them on, and started to skate home. She still wished she were old enough to have a car or rich enough to own a bicycle.

When Penelope got home, her mom and dad were in the kitchen. "I didn't have enough money for a bicycle," she said. "All I could buy were roller skates."

"Roller skates are the best wheels a kid can have," said her dad.

"Skating is better than walking," she said, "but I still wish I had a bike."

The next day Penelope was going to the ball park to watch the big softball game. The Brave Bears were playing the Terrible Tigers. They were the best two teams in town. Everyone would be there.

As she sat on the grass putting on her roller skates, Mr. Smith came out of his house and got into his car.

"Are you going to the game?" Penelope asked.

"I sure am," said Mr. Smith.

"I'm skating to the game," said Penelope.

"Be sure you don't get any tickets for going too fast!" he said.

Penelope skated toward the ball park. Her friend Jim rode by on his bicycle.

"Going to the game?" she asked.

"Yes," he said.

"I am, too," said Penelope.

"Let's race," said Jim.

Penelope skated as fast as she could, but Jim went faster. Soon he turned the corner and she couldn't see him at all.

When Penelope got to the corner that the ball park was on, she stopped. There were cars everywhere! Everyone was trying to find a parking space.

Penelope skated right by Mr. Smith. "I didn't get any tickets for going too fast," she said.

"Really!" Mr. Smith laughed.

Then Penelope saw Jim. He was looking for a place to leave his bike. She skated by him. "Does the winner get a prize?" she called.

Penelope took off her skates and went to find a seat.

Soon the umpire shouted, "PLAY BALL!"

Right after that, Jim walked by looking for a seat.

It was the second inning before Mr. Smith came in.

Penelope laughed and thought to herself, "Roller skates really are the best wheels a kid can have."

Story Wrap-up

Summary Questions

Penelope wanted wheels. These questions will help you tell what Penelope learned.

1. Why didn't Penelope get a car or a bicycle?
2. What did Penelope buy instead? How did she feel about buying them?
3. What did Penelope learn about her wheels? How did she learn this?

The Reading and Writing Connection

Pretend you own a store that sells roller skates. Make a sign that tells why people should buy your skates. Use some of these words.

really	**birthday**	**ticket**
cost	**ninety**	**guess**

Vocabulary

Which Meaning?

Many words have more than one meaning. When you see the word *park* by itself, you cannot tell what the word means.

If the word *park* is in a sentence, some of the other words in the sentence will help you know which meaning to use.

Which meaning of *park* is used in each sentence below? Use the words with a line under them to help you.

1. Mom said she was going to <u>stop</u> and **park** by the <u>side of the road</u>.
2. We went to the **park** to <u>play ball</u>.

In which sentence does *park* mean "something that is done with a car"? In which sentence does *park* mean "a piece of land"?

The other words in the sentence helped you to know which meaning of *park* was being used.

Read each pair of sentences below. Then decide which sentence tells about the picture.

1. We must carefully follow the **steps** for making this airplane.

2. We are sitting on the **steps.**

3. My mother gave me this **bill** to buy some eggs.

4. That bird has a long **bill.**

Which words in the sentences helped you figure out the meanings of the words in heavy black letters?

Reading in Social Studies: Textbook

ON LAND AND IN THE AIR

People travel from place to place in many different ways. They use different kinds of transportation. How many different kinds of transportation do you know about?

Why do people need different kinds of transportation? People need to travel to different places—some near, some far away.

People who live outside a big city may want to go into the city to work, to shop, or to have fun. They can drive their cars into the city, or they can take a **bus** or a **train.**

How do people get around a big city once they get there? In most cities they can travel by car or they can take a bus. In some cities they can take another kind of train – a **subway.** A subway is a train that runs through tunnels under the ground. A subway can travel very fast because it does not have to stop for cars and buses on the street.

In some cities, people can travel by **monorail.** A monorail is a train that runs on only one rail. Sometimes the rail is on the ground, but most of the time it is above the ground. The monorail can travel above busy streets and over water.

How can people travel to far away places quickly? They can travel by air. Huge **jet planes** take thousands of people all over the world every day. Jet planes are very fast, and they can carry a lot of people. These planes take off and land in special places called airports.

A **helicopter** is another kind of air transportation. It can't go as fast or as far as a jet plane, but it can do many things a jet plane cannot do. It can fly straight up and down and sideways. It can even stay in one place and turn around.

The newest and fastest way to travel is in a **rocket.** At first only astronauts traveled by rocket, but now other people are being given a chance to travel this way.

Selection Wrap-up

Summary Questions

1. Why do people need different kinds of transportation?
2. Name some different ways people can travel into the city.
3. Name some different ways of traveling once a person gets to the city.
4. What is a subway?
5. How is a monorail different from a subway?
6. What can a helicopter do that an airplane cannot do?

Transportation Activity

Make a transportation picture.
On a large piece of paper, draw the land and the sky. Then draw, or cut out and glue onto paper, pictures of different kinds of transportation. Place the pictures where they belong.

Skill
Cause – Effect

Often one thing will happen in a story because of something else that has already happened. It will help you to understand the story if you know how one thing causes another to happen.

Read what the man in the picture is saying.

It is raining and the man's car has a flat tire. Which of those things might cause the man to say he has to take the bus to work?

You know that people drive their cars in the rain all the time. But you know that when a car has a flat tire, the car is usually not driven until the tire is changed. That is what caused the man to say he would have to take the bus to work.

Using what you read and what you know about cars with flat tires helped you to figure out what caused something to happen.

Now read the story below.

Mary had wanted a dog for a long time and she knew just what kind she wanted. She wanted a big black dog. So on the day that her father surprised her with a little white dog named Fluff, Mary felt a little sad. To make things worse, Fluff followed Mary *everywhere* she went.

One day when Mary was riding her bike, she fell off and cut her leg. How she wished she had a way to let her mother know what had happened.

Just as she was trying to decide what to do, Fluff ran off. A few minutes later, Mary saw her mother and Fluff running down the street.

"I knew something must have happened when Fluff came back without you," said Mary's mother.

"Thank you, Fluff," said Mary. "I am very glad that you are my dog."

Now answer these questions.

1. What caused Mary to feel sad when she saw Fluff?
2. What caused Mary to hurt her leg?
3. What caused Mary's mother to come running down the street?
4. What caused Mary to say that she was very glad that Fluff was her dog?

Skill Summary

When you are reading, it will be easier for you to understand what you are reading if you think about how one thing causes something else to happen. Use what you read and what you already know to help you.

The Great Hamster Hunt

by Lenore Blegvad

When Nicholas takes care of Harvey the hamster, he learns what *nocturnal* means. How does the meaning of this word help Nicholas?

Nicholas wanted a hamster, but his mother and father said, "No."

"Tony has a hamster," Nicholas said.

His mother and father still said, "No."

Then one day Tony came to the door. "We're going away for a week," he said to Nicholas. "Would you take care of my hamster for me?"

"Yes!" Nicholas shouted. "I would love to take care of your hamster."

So Tony's hamster, Harvey, came to stay with Nicholas. It lived in a nice big cage. The cage had wire on the top and a wall of glass on the front. There was also a wheel that went around and around when Harvey ran inside it.

Before Tony left, he told Nicholas how to take care of Harvey. Once Tony was on the other side of the street, he stopped and called to Nicholas. "Just in case you didn't know," he said, "hamsters are nocturnal."

"What does that mean?" Nicholas called back. But Tony was gone.

All that week Nicholas took good care of Harvey. He fed him and played with him. He cleaned his cage carefully.

Harvey seemed to sleep most of the day, but at night he loved to run around inside his wheel.

All too soon the week was up and Tony would be coming home the next evening. After supper, Nicholas decided to clean Harvey's cage for the last time. He took the cage down to the kitchen.

First he put Harvey into a large box, where he could watch him. Then, very carefully, he slid the glass from the cage. He started to put it on the kitchen table, when all of a sudden the glass fell from his hands and broke into a thousand pieces all over the kitchen floor!

Nicholas's father helped to clean up the pieces. Then his father found a piece of heavy cardboard. He cut it to fit in the cage. He slid the cardboard into the place where the glass had been. Nicholas put Harvey back into the cage.

By now it was time for Nicholas to go to bed. "Good night, Harvey," he said. "We sure had a good time, didn't we?" Then he turned out his light and soon fell asleep.

The next morning, Nicholas looked in through the top of the cage to say, "Good morning," but ... *the cage was empty*!

"Oh, no!" Mother said when Nicholas told her.

"Oh, no!" Father said when he went to see.

So they began to look – right then, before breakfast. They looked all over the room, but they did not find Harvey.

Then Mother said, "He could be anywhere, not just here in your room."

"I have an idea." said Father as he hurried out of the room. When Father came back, he was carrying six wastebaskets and some boards. He asked Nicholas to get him some lettuce.

First he put a small pile of books in each room in the house. Next he leaned a wastebasket on each pile of books. Then he took the boards and the lettuce and he made . . . hamster traps!

"Now all we have to do is wait for Harvey to eat his way up the board and fall into one of the plastic wastebaskets," Father said. "He will slip on the plastic if he tries to climb out."

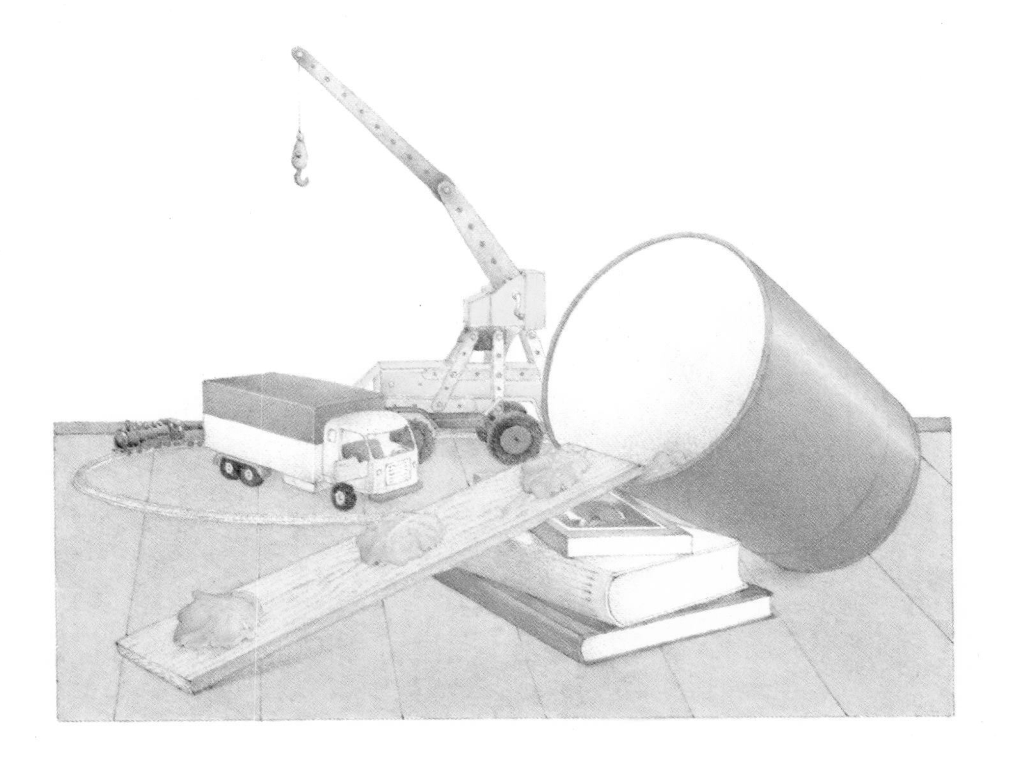

Mother said, "We'd better go shopping, just in case." So Mother and Nicholas went to the pet store.

"We need a white hamster," she said.

"I'm sorry," the pet store owner said. "We have only brown hamsters. Will they do?"

"No," Mother said. "They won't do. We'll try another pet store."

And they did. They tried many other pet stores. When they got to the very last one, they were happy to see a white hamster that looked very much like Harvey.

"We'll take that one," Mother said. She also bought a piece of glass for Harvey's cage. The store owner put the hamster in a little cardboard box that had holes in the top. Nicholas held the box very carefully all the way home. He felt much better now. Tony wouldn't have Harvey, but he would have a hamster.

When they got home, Nicholas put the new hamster in Harvey's cage. It ran around the wheel a few times and then it went to sleep. "I hope Tony will get to like you as much as he liked Harvey," Nicholas said to the hamster. "Anyway, I like you. I wish you were my hamster."

"I don't know about *you,*" Mother said, "but I'm tired. I am going to play some quiet music."

"A nocturne would be nice," Father said. Nicholas turned his head.

"A *what*?" he asked. Where had he heard that word before?

"A nocturne is a piece of night music, a dreamy kind of music," said Father. "The word *nocturne* has to do with night."

"Then that's what Tony meant!" Nicholas cried. "That's why Harvey sleeps all day and plays all night. That's what hamsters do. They're nocturnal!"

Nicholas ran into the dark kitchen, where, sure enough, the new hamster had awakened. He was running around Harvey's wheel, just as Harvey used to do at night.

"Now that it's nighttime, it's time to look for Harvey," Nicholas shouted. He ran into his dark room and sat down on the bed.

As Nicholas listened to the nocturne that his mother was playing, he was also listening for another sound. Then he heard it. It came from under his bookcase. Nicholas turned on his light, just in time to see Harvey's head poking out from behind the bookcase.

Nicholas waited until Harvey was all the way out into the room, and then he picked him up.

"I've got him! I've got him!" he called to his mother and father.

"Good for you," Father said.

Nicholas put Harvey back into his cage. The two hamsters looked at each other for a long time. Then the new hamster started running around the wheel again and Harvey ate some lettuce.

As Nicholas watched the hamsters, he felt a feeling of hope. He looked at his mother and father.

"Do you think . . . " he began, "if I took very good care of him . . . that maybe . . . ?"

"Yes," his father said. "You know so much about hamsters I don't see why you shouldn't have one of your own."

His mother said, "We'll get him a cage in the morning. Tonight he can sleep in Harvey's cage."

The next day, Tony came to the door. He had come for Harvey. He was very surprised to see another white hamster in Harvey's cage. Nicholas took his new hamster out, and it ran up his arm to sit on his shoulder.

Tony asked, "Was it your birthday? Is that when you got your hamster?"

Nicholas shook his head. "No," he said happily. "I got him just by accident."

"Oh," was all Tony said. He picked up Harvey's cage and walked to the door.

"Well, thanks a lot for taking care of Harvey for me," said Tony.

"Anytime," said Nicholas.

In the mirror next to the front door, Nicholas saw himself with his hamster. The hamster was sitting on Nicholas's shoulder. It looked very happy up there. Nicholas looked happy, too.

Story Wrap-up

Summary Questions

These questions will help you tell how Nicholas got a hamster of his own.

1. Why do you think Nicholas's mother and father wouldn't let him have a hamster of his own at first?
2. Do you think Nicholas took good care of Harvey? Why or why not?
3. How did taking care of Harvey help Nicholas get his own hamster?
4. What if Nicholas was going away and needed a friend to take care of his hamster for a week? What things would Nicholas tell his friend about hamsters?

The Reading and Writing Connection

Pretend you are Harvey. Tell the new hamster about Nicholas and what happened to you at Nicholas's house. Write what you think Harvey would say. Use some of the words in the box.

hamster	**hunt**	**lettuce**
nocturnal	**cage**	**awakened**
climb	**traps**	**accident**

Hamsters

by Marci Ridlon

Hamsters are the nicest things
That anyone could own.
I like them even better than
Some dogs that I have known.

Their fur is soft, their faces nice.
They're small when they are grown.
And they sit inside your pocket
When you are all alone.

Magazine Wrap-up

Good Things Happen

Each of the characters you read about in Magazine Three had a problem.

Jasper didn't know how to become a ______.
Martha and Peter didn't have any ______.
Penelope didn't have enough ______.
Nicholas couldn't have a ______.

Tell how each problem was solved.

Word Watch

Match each word with its meaning.

jet	**train that moves on one rail**
subway	**dreamy, night music**
monorail	**fast airplane**
nocturne	**underground train**

Use each word in a sentence.

A Favorite Character

Think about the characters you read about in Magazine Three. Which did you like best? Write some sentences telling about your favorite character and what you liked about that character.

Books to Enjoy 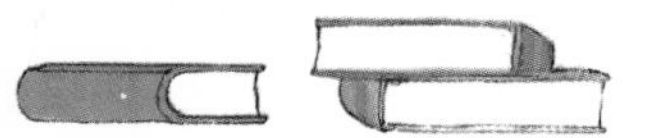

Aunt Nina and her Nephews and Nieces
by Franz Brandenburg

There are surprises and fun when Aunt Nina plans a birthday party for her cat.

George and Martha Back in Town
by James Marshall

Here are five short stories about two hippos who are the best of friends.

Rainy Sunday by Eleanor Schick

On a rainy Sunday in the city, Jill has fun at home with her mother and father.

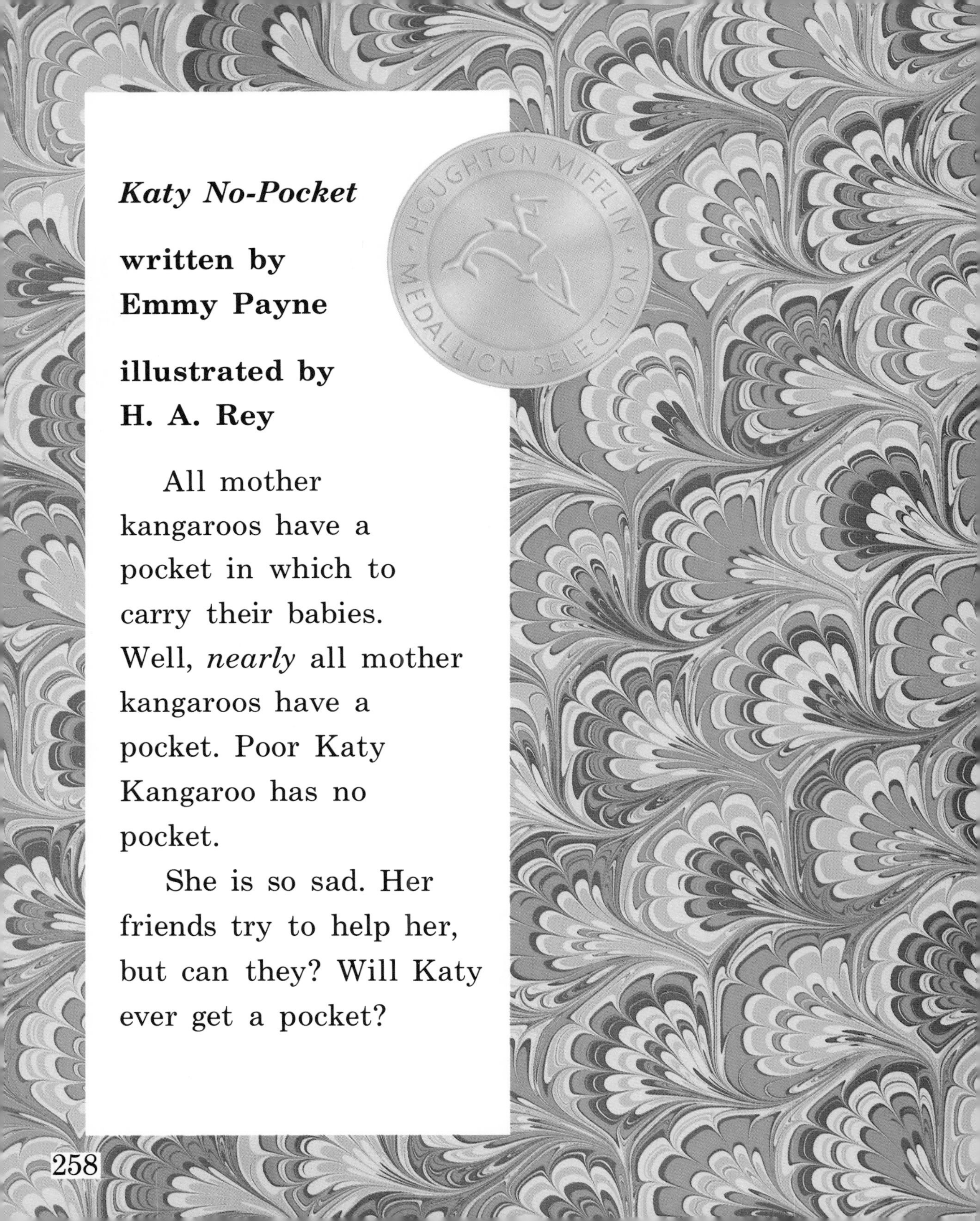

Katy No-Pocket

written by
Emmy Payne

illustrated by
H. A. Rey

All mother kangaroos have a pocket in which to carry their babies. Well, *nearly* all mother kangaroos have a pocket. Poor Katy Kangaroo has no pocket.

She is so sad. Her friends try to help her, but can they? Will Katy ever get a pocket?

Katy No-Pocket

Story by Emmy Payne

Pictures by H. A. Rey

Big tears rolled down Katy Kangaroo's brown face. Poor Katy didn't have a pocket like other mother kangaroos. Freddy was Katy Kangaroo's little boy and he needed a pocket to ride in. Grown-up kangaroos take very big hops. Little kangaroos, like Freddy, get left behind when their mothers don't have pockets to carry them in. Poor Katy didn't have any pocket at all.

Then, all of a sudden, Katy had a wonderful idea! The idea was this. Other animal mothers had children and they didn't have any pockets. She'd go and ask one of them how they carried their babies!

"I'll ask Mrs. Crocodile," said Katy. So Katy and Freddy went down to the river.

When Mrs. Crocodile saw Katy, she said, "Why, Katy Kangaroo! What can I do for you today?"

"Please, Mrs. Crocodile, I'm so sad," said Katy. "I have no pocket, and Freddy has to walk wherever we go. He gets so tired. How do you carry little Catherine Crocodile?"

"I carry her on my back, of course!" said Mrs. Crocodile. "That is the right way to carry babies."

Katy was very pleased. Now she knew how to carry Freddy. As soon as she got to a good place, she bent down and said, "Hop up on my back, Freddy. From now on, it will be easy for us to get around."

But it wasn't easy. When Freddy finally did get up on Katy's back, it was hard for him to hold on. When he did manage to hold on for a few seconds, and Katy gave a long hop, he fell off – *bump, bump . . . bump*!

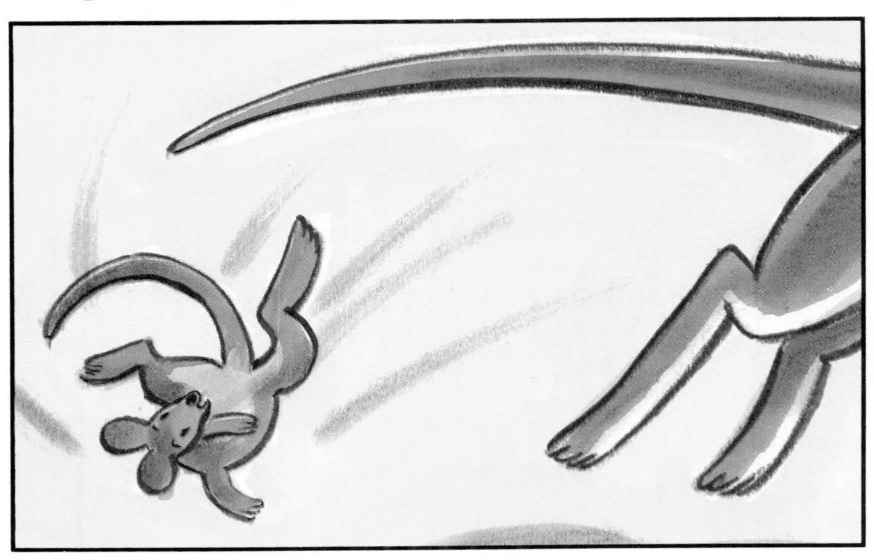

Katy saw that she couldn't carry her baby on her back. She and Freddy sat down again and thought and thought.

"I know! I'll ask Mrs. Monkey. I'm sure she can help me."

So Katy and Freddy went off to the forest and very soon they found Mrs. Monkey and her baby, Jocko.

"Please, Mrs. Monkey, tell me how you carry Jocko," said Katy.

"In my arms, of course," said Mrs. Monkey. Then she jumped away through the trees.

"Oh, dear," said Katy. "I can't carry anything in these little arms. Mrs. Monkey wasn't any help at all."

Then Freddy said, "What about the lions?"

"They don't carry their children. The poor things walk just the way you do," said Katy.

Then all at once Katy looked at Freddy. "They do say that Mrs. Owl knows almost everything," she said slowly.

"Then let's go and ask Mrs. Owl!" said Freddy.

They found Mrs. Owl asleep in an old tree. She was angry because she didn't want to be awakened. But when she saw that Katy was so sad, she came out and said, "Well! Well! What is it?"

"I'm a mother kangaroo," said Katy, "and I haven't a pocket to carry my little boy in. How shall I carry him? What shall I do?"

"*Get* a pocket," said Mrs. Owl and then she went back to sleep again.

"Where?" cried Katy. "Oh, please, don't go to sleep before you tell me where!"

"How should I know?" said Mrs. Owl. "They sell that kind of thing in the City, I believe. Now please go away and let me sleep."

"The City!" said Katy, "Of course, we'll go to the City!"

Katy was so happy. She hopped so fast that Freddy could hardly keep up, but at last they arrived in the City where there were shops and houses and cars and people.

The people all stared and stared at Katy, but she didn't care.

She was looking for pockets and she saw that almost everybody had them. Then, all at once, she saw – she could hardly believe it – a man who seemed to be ALL pockets! He was covered with pockets . . . big pockets, little pockets, short pockets, long pockets!

When Katy went up to him, he seemed a little scared at first. Then Katy looked at him with her soft brown eyes and asked, "Please, dear, kind man, where did you get all those pockets?"

"They just came with the apron, of course," he said. "I keep my tools in my pockets, but I can get another apron, so I'll give you mine."

He took off the apron and dumped it UPSIDE DOWN. Out fell all his tools. Then the man turned it right side up again and put it around Katy.

Katy was so pleased and happy that she couldn't say a word. She just looked down at the pockets and smiled.

At last Katy was able to say "Thank you" to the nice, kind man, . . . and then what do you think she did? She popped Freddy into a pocket, and she hopped home faster than ever before. This time, of course, she didn't have to wait for Freddy.

When she got home, what do you think she did?

Well, she had so many pockets that she put Freddy into the biggest one of all. Then, into the next biggest pocket she put little Jocko Monkey. Catherine Crocodile just fit into another pocket.

There was still room for a rabbit, an owl, a lion, a turtle, and a frog.

So now, all the animals like Katy's pockets better than any other pockets in the whole forest.

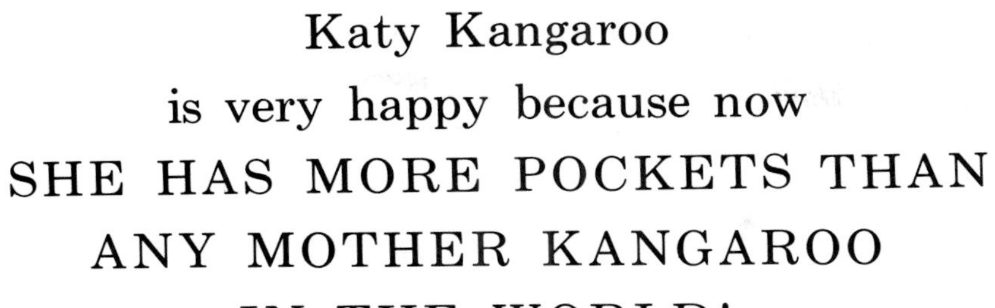
Katy Kangaroo
is very happy because now
SHE HAS MORE POCKETS THAN
ANY MOTHER KANGAROO
IN THE WORLD!

Summary Questions

1. Who helped Katy with her problem? Tell how.
2. Why was it important for Katy to have a pocket?
3. Which do you think would be best for a kangaroo to have — one pocket as most mother kangaroos do, or many pockets as Katy has? Tell why.

Author

Emmy Payne was the name used by Emily West when she wrote the picture book *Katy No-Pocket.* This book has been a favorite among children for a long time.

Illustrator

H. A. Rey was born in Germany in 1898. He came to America with his wife in 1940. The Reys are best known for their *Curious George* books, two of which have won prizes.

Glossary

A

afternoon I walk home from school in the ***afternoon.***

airports Most airplanes take off and land in ***airports.***

alone I like to play with other children more than I like to play ***alone.***

apron He didn't want to get dirty, so he put on an ***apron*** when he cooked.

arrived Everyday she ***arrived*** at school at the same time.

astronauts The three ***astronauts*** traveled in a rocket ship.

B

balancing My friend tried ***balancing*** a book on his head.

bicycle Will rode his new ***bicycle*** to school.

blocks The children like to play with the ***blocks*** by placing them one on top of the other.

board I put my picture up on the ***board*** so everyone could see it.

brave The ***brave*** girl found her way out of the dark woods.

breathe People ***breathe*** air while most fish can ***breathe*** under the water.

bunch I gave my friend a ***bunch*** of flowers.

C

cabbage I like to eat the ***cabbage*** from my garden.

catch You throw the ball, and I will ***catch*** it.

caught She threw the ball, and I ***caught*** it.

cheered We ***cheered*** when my brother finished first in the race.

closed Lisa ***closed*** the window when it started to rain.

club My mother is in a sports ***club.***

clue The detective found a ***clue*** in the house.

coins Sometimes ***coins*** are used to pay for things.

corner Our house is on the ***corner*** of the street.

cost The book you want will ***cost*** four dollars.

costumes Shawn and Pam decided to wear the funny ***costumes.***

crowd There was such a big ***crowd*** at the game, we couldn't find seats.

crutches Judy uses her ***crutches*** to help her walk.

curves The street has many ***curves*** in it.

D

different The ugly duck looked ***different*** from the other ducks.

doctor We called the ***doctor*** when my brother was sick.

dominoes I like to play ***dominoes*** with my friends.

doorstep I waited on the ***doorstep*** of his house.

dump I went to the ***dump*** and threw away some things I didn't want anymore.

E

easy It was ***easy*** for the librarian to find the book I needed.

edge Ann sat down on the ***edge*** of the bed.

elves The little ***elves*** in my storybook have big ears.

empty I want more milk because my glass is ***empty.***

end I liked the story so much, I did not want it to ***end.***

engine The shiny red fire ***engine*** raced by us on its way to the fire.

enjoy I ***enjoy*** drawing pictures.

expected I ***expected*** to find books in the library.

F

faint When I saw the big monster in the movie, I thought I would ***faint.***

far We cannot walk to her house because it is too ***far*** away.

farola A ***farola*** is a kind of lantern you might see in some parades.

farther The ***farther*** we walked into the woods, the more lost we got.

favorite Brown is my *favorite* color.

few There were only a *few* ducks in the pond.

filled I ***filled*** the pail with water.

finally It has ***finally*** stopped raining.

firefighter The brave ***firefighter*** helped put out the fire.

fruits Of all the ***fruits,*** I like oranges best.

G

gentle Nate's father told him to be ***gentle*** when he held the baby.

giraffe A ***giraffe*** is an animal with a long neck and long legs.

gobbled I was so hungry, I ***gobbled*** up my lunch.

H

hamster A ***hamster*** is a little animal that some people have as a pet.

helicopter I watched the ***helicopter*** fly up and down and sideways.

hero Susan was a ***hero*** for bringing home the lost dog.

hid We all ***hid*** under the table.

huge The ***huge*** dog ran after the little cat.

hurt I fell when I was skating and ***hurt*** my foot.

I

inning We were late for the game, so we missed the first ***inning.***

invisible The ghost was ***invisible*** so you could not see it.

J

jet We saw a ***jet*** plane land at the airport.

job It is his ***job*** to help children find books in the school library.

join We asked Robert to ***join*** us in the game we were playing.

K

kangaroo The tiny baby ***kangaroo*** climbed into its mother's pocket.

L

leaned Tina ***leaned*** her bicycle against the house.

line We stood in ***line*** to wait for the bus.

lions ***Lions*** cannot be pets because they are animals who live in the forest.

lose If I ***lose*** my pencil, I will not be able to write.

M

map A ***map*** can show you how to get from one place to another.

means When it rains, it ***means*** we can't play outside.

meeting We all had a ***meeting*** to decide who would be captain of our baseball team.

message The ***message*** on the card said, "Get well".

midnight My bedtime is way before ***midnight.***

mine The picture of the rabbit is ***mine.***

mirror I can see myself in the ***mirror.***

monorail A ***monorail*** train moves on one rail.

mumps My sister is sick with the ***mumps.***

music John always says listening to ***music*** makes him happy.

N

napkins Before supper, it is my job to put the tablecloth and ***napkins*** on the table.

neck A giraffe has a very long ***neck.***

nocturnal The hamster sleeps all day and stays awake all night because it is ***nocturnal.***

nocturne My father likes music and listens to a ***nocturne*** every evening.

P

pails I helped carry the ***pails*** that were filled with water.

pair Dad cannot find his favorite ***pair*** of shoes.

park My teacher likes to walk through the ***park*** and look at all the trees and flowers.

path We walked on the ***path*** through the woods.

perhaps If I win a prize, ***perhaps*** I will give it to my brother.

photograph The ***photograph*** of the frog looked a lot like the picture I drew.

piece She did not want all of the sandwich, so she ate only a ***piece*** of it.

pile I picked up a ***pile*** of papers from the table.

plastic The ***plastic*** plate did not break when it fell off the table.

poking The rabbit was ***poking*** its nose through the fence.

popped The frog ***popped*** its head out of the water.

price The ***price*** of that coat is too high for me to buy it.

promise If I ***promise*** to do my homework, may I go to the movies?

Q

quickly The frog jumped ***quickly*** into the pond.

quite Henry was not ***quite*** finished eating his breakfast.

R

river We like to watch boats on the ***river.***

rocket A ***rocket*** is faster than a jet plane.

S

sang We played music and ***sang*** songs.

sea The boats waited to go to ***sea.***

secret I cannot tell you what I know because it is a ***secret.***

seemed He ***seemed*** happy, but then he started to cry.

seen I wish I had ***seen*** the fish jump out of the water.

shoelaces Some shoes have ***shoelaces.***

shop We looked at all the books in the ***shop*** window.

sill Put the plant on the window ***sill.***

skill Balancing a ball on your head takes a lot of ***skill.***

slid We ***slid*** down the hill.

slippery Wet rocks are sometimes very ***slippery.***

snow We went outside to play in the ***snow.***

softball Let's play a game of ***softball.***

space There was ***space*** at the table for two more people.

spaghetti Dad fixed ***spaghetti*** for supper.

spent I ***spent*** the day at the park.

spray You should ***spray*** water on the garden to help it grow.

spread I always ***spread*** butter on my bread.

spun The wheels of the bicycle ***spun*** around and around.

stared The hungry dog ***stared*** at the biscuit I was eating.

stomped Clara ***stomped*** through the puddles and got me wet.

straight Peter drew a ***straight*** line under his name.

string You need to put a ***string*** on my kite before you can fly it.

stuck My little brother is ***stuck*** up in the tree.

subway A ***subway*** carries people underground.

sudden The ***sudden*** cry of the bear cubs scared the mother bear.

symbol The ***symbol*** for a library may be a picture of a book.

T

tears When Peter cried, ***tears*** rolled down his face.

terrible Ira felt ***terrible*** when he lost his new book.

through We walked ***through*** the woods.

tide We could see the rocks before the ***tide*** came in and covered them with water.

tools I used my ***tools*** to build a birdhouse.

tossed Ana ***tossed*** the ball to me.

touched I ***touched*** the rabbit and it ran away.

toward We walked ***toward*** the pond.

tower The tall ***tower*** was bigger than any of the houses in the picture.

trotting We saw the little dog ***trotting*** toward its doghouse.

tub I filled the ***tub*** with water.

tunnels In a city, some trains ride through the ***tunnels*** under the streets.

turnip I ate a ***turnip*** from the garden for supper.

U

umpire Laurie missed the ball three times and the ***umpire*** called, "Out!"

understand Max could not ***understand*** why the kite would not fly.

V

vegetables We grew ***vegetables*** in the garden.

village Tonight there is going to be a party in the ***village*** where I live.

violin Ana was learning to play the ***violin.***

W

waved Jimmy ***waved*** good-by when he left.

winter On cold and snowy ***winter*** days, we play inside.

wire The hamster's cage is made of ***wire.***

wondered She ***wondered*** where she put her hat.

world Some airplanes fly all over the ***world.***

Student Handbook

Read
Write
Listen
Speak

Reading Unknown Words

When you come to a new word —

- Read to the end of the sentence.
- Think about what the sentence is saying.
- Think about the sounds the letters stand for.
- Then ask, "Does the word make sense? Does it have the right sounds?"

Sounds You Know – Consonants

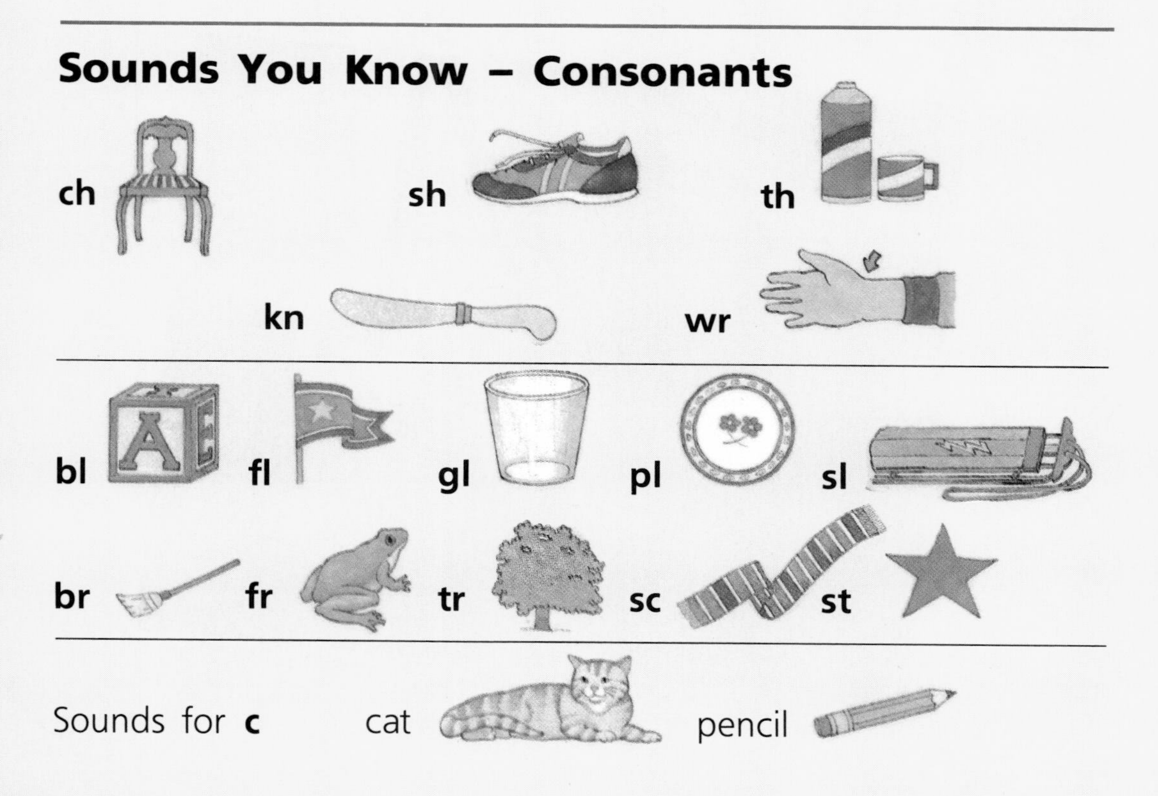

New Sounds – Consonants

qu **squ**  **thr** **spr**  **str** 

Sounds for **g** game  giraffe 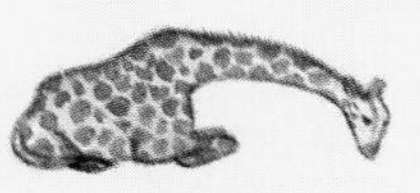

More Sounds You Know – Vowels

short **a** 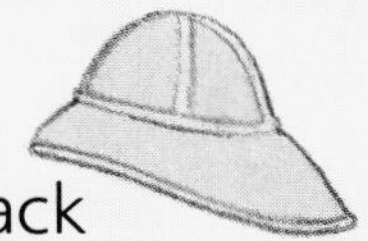

can am back

long **a**

make ate name

short **e** 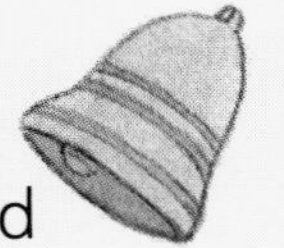

went egg red

long **e** 

feet each we

short **i** 

his if with

long **i** 

time idea five

short **o** 

stop off got

long **o** 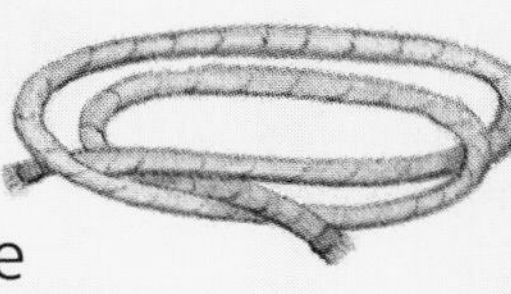

coat over home

short **u** 

cut up run

long **u** 

cute use huge

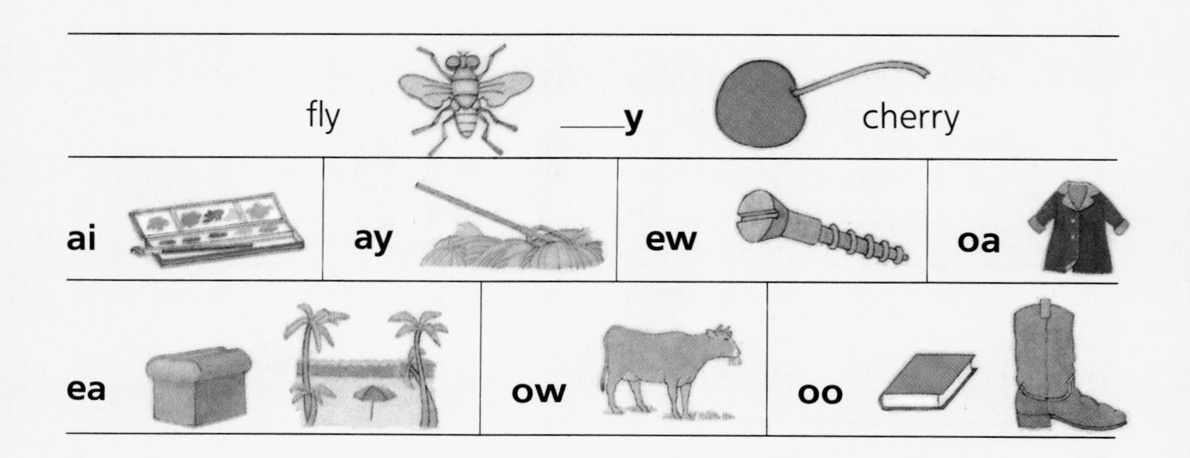

New Sounds – Vowels

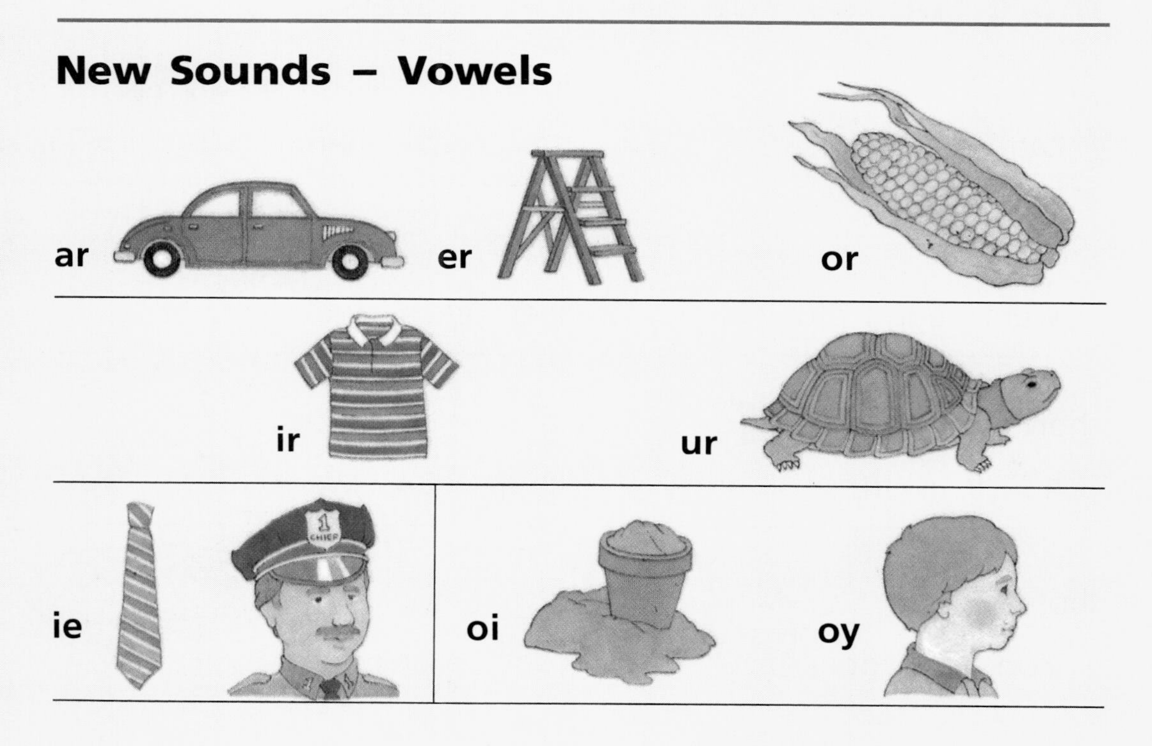

Reading Stories

When you read a story, you read for fun. You read to find out about the people or animals in the story. You want to understand the story. Use these ideas to understand and remember the stories you read.

Before You Read

1 Read the title, and look at the pictures.

- What do the title and pictures tell you about the story?
- What do you think the story will be about?
- What do you already know about the topic?

2 Read the author's name.

- Have you read any other stories by this author? What were those stories about?

➡

3. **Think about the kinds of things you want to find out in a story.**
   - Who is in the story?
   - Where does the story take place?
   - What happens in the story?

While You Read

1. **Remember the most important things that happen.**
2. **Think about what might happen next.**
3. **Read to find out if it does or does not happen.**
4. **Ask questions about the story.**
   - Does the story make sense to you?
   - Are there any parts you do not understand?
5. **Read parts of the story again if you need to.**

After You Read

1 Think about what happened in the story.

- What were the most important things that happened? Why did they happen?

2 Think about how the story made you feel.

- Did you like the story? Why or why not?
- Did you like anyone in the story? Why? Was there someone you did not like? Why?
- Would you like to read other stories by this author? Why?

3 Think about things in the story that might happen to you.

- Has something in the story ever happened to you? What did you do?

4 Think about other stories.

- How was this story like others you have read? How was it different?

Reading to Learn

Reading is one of the best ways to learn about something. Use these ideas to understand and remember what you read.

Before You Read

1 Look over what you will read.

- Read the title.
- Look at the pictures.

2 Think about the topic.

- What do you already know about it?
- What do you think you will find out?

While You Read

1 Think about what you are learning.

- Find important things to remember about the topic.
- Find important words to remember.

2. **Ask yourself questions about the topic.**
3. **Be sure you understand what you read.**
   - Go back and read again any parts you do not understand.

Reading in Science: Textbook

HOW BIG IS BIG?

Animals live in all parts of the world. They come in many sizes. Some animals are so tiny that you can't see them. Some are so huge that it's hard to even picture them in your mind. Find out just how big some animals are.

102

After You Read

1. **Think about what you have learned.**
   - What was the topic?
   - What important things did you learn about this topic? Did you learn some important words?
2. **Answer the questions you asked as you were reading.**
3. **Think about the topic.**
   - Did you like what you read? What else do you want to know about this topic?

Write

The Writing Process

1 Prewriting

Before you begin to write, decide what topic you want to write about.

- Make a list of ideas.
- Think about each idea on your list.
  - Do you know enough to write about it?
  - Is there too much to tell?
  - Would your readers like to know about it?
- Decide which idea is best to write about.
- Circle the idea. It will be your topic.

airplane trip
baseball game
street carnival

Paul wanted to write to Grandfather about something they had done together. Paul listed some ideas. He circled the best one.

After you pick your topic, make a plan for your story. Here are some things to do to plan.

- Write a sentence about your topic.
- Think about things to tell.
- Draw pictures about your topic.
- Write as many words about the topic as you can.

Here is Paul's plan.

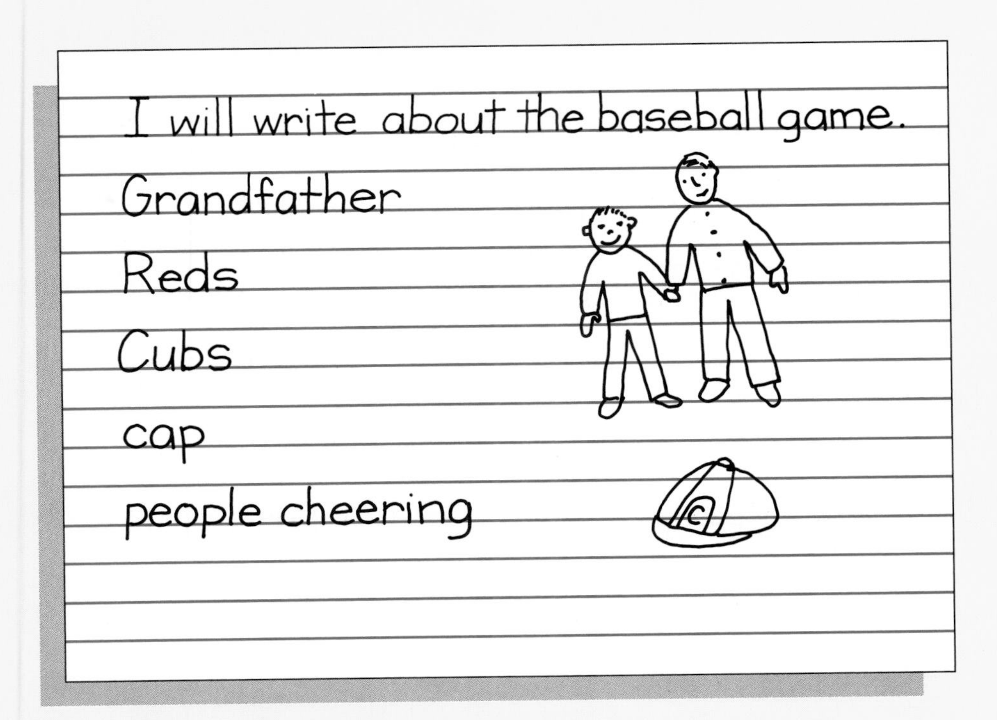

② Write a First Draft

After you have a plan, write a first draft of your story. A first draft is a first try.

- Follow your plan to write your story. Do not worry about mistakes. You can make changes later.

Here is Paul's first draft. He left room to make changes.

I want to a big baseball game. I want with my grandfather. The Game was at nite. The Cubs and reds played I got a Cubs cap. The ~~people~~ croud cheer.

❸ Revise

When you revise, look at your story to make changes.

- Read your story to yourself.
  Can you add anything?
  Should you leave anything out?
- Change words and sentences to make your story better.
- Read your story to a friend. Listen to what your friend says and asks.
- Revise your story to make it clearer.

Paul read his story to Laura. She listened.

Laura: I like the part about the Cubs cap.
Paul: Should I tell more about anything?
Laura: You can tell who won.
Paul: Okay. I'll add that.
Laura: How do you see a game at night?

Paul made some changes. He thought about what Laura had said. Then he revised his story some more.

I want to a big baseball game. ~~I want~~ with my grandfather. The Game was at nite. There were lots of big lights. The Cubs and reds played. We cheered for the Cubs. I got a Cubs cap. The Cubs won 4 to 3. The ~~people~~ croud cheer. and shouted when the Cubs got the last run.

❹ Proofread

Read your story again. Check for mistakes, and fix them.

- Use this checklist and these special marks to fix your mistakes.

Proofreading Checklist

☑ 1. Did I begin each sentence with a capital letter?

☑ 2. Did I use correct end marks?

☑ 3. Did I spell each word correctly?

Proofreading Marks

^ Add.

Take out.

≡ Make a capital letter.

/ Make a small letter.

Here is Paul's proofread story.

I ~~want~~ went to a big baseball game. ~~I want~~ with my grandfather. The Game was at ~~nite~~ night. There were lots of big lights. The Cubs and reds played. We cheered for the Cubs. I got a Cubs cap. The Cubs won 4 to 3. The ~~people~~ ~~croud~~ crowd cheered and shouted when the Cubs got the last run.

❺ Publish

When you want to share what you have written, make a final copy.

- Copy your story in your best handwriting.
- Proofread once again. Fix any mistakes.
- Think of a special way to share your work.

Paul made a drawing to go with his story. He sent them to his grandfather.

I went to a big baseball game with my grandfather. The game was at night. There were lots of big lights. The Cubs and Reds played. We cheered for the Cubs. I got a Cubs cap. The Cubs won 4 to 3. The crowd cheered and shouted when the Cubs got the last home run.

by Paul Ling

Listen and Speak

Listening

You listen to find out about new things. Use these ideas to help you understand and remember what you hear.

- Pay attention to what the speaker says.
- Listen for important new words.
- Listen to answer the questions *Who? What? Where? When?*
- Ask questions if you do not understand.

Giving a Talk

When you give a talk, you want to tell about something interesting. You want your listeners to learn something. Use these ideas to help you give a talk.

- Plan what you will say.
- Make your talk interesting.
- Speak loudly and clearly.
- Look at the class or group.
- Do not say ah or um.

Discussing Writing

After you have written a story, read it aloud to a friend. You and your listener can discuss the writing to make it better.

1 The writer can ask these questions.

- Did you understand my story?
- Is there anything else you would like to know?

2 The listener should follow these steps.

- Listen carefully.
- Tell something you liked about the story, or tell something you heard.
- Ask questions if you did not understand something.
- Be polite.

Continued from page 2.

Credits

Cover and title page illustrated by Kathy Mitchell
Magazine openers illustrated by Kristina Rodanas

Illustrators: **8–9** Kristina Rodanas **12–20** Linda Strauss Edwards **21** Jan Brett **22–37** Jose Aruego & Ariane Dewey **38–41** Lynn Cherry **42–53** Diana Magnuson **54–55, 62–65** Maxie Chambliss **67–76** (illustrations) Arnold Lobel (borders) © Gibbons **77** Lynn Cherry **80–81** Kristina Rodanas **84–100** Karen Locciasano **101** Carl Schwartz **102–107** Terry Riley **108–109** Maxie Chambliss **110–119** Mai Vo-Dinh **120** Carol Schwartz **121–132** Derek Steele **133–136** Chris Czernota **137–152** Anthony Accardo **153–158** Leo Abbett **159–163** Lynn Cherry **164–175** Carol Leeson **178–179** Kristina Rodanas **182–194** Eric Jon Nones **195–198** Lynn Cherry **199–214** David Wenzel **215** Stella Ormai **216–225** Susanna Natti **226–237** Lynn Cherry **238–254** Diet Van Beek **225**Alan Baker **258–273** (illustrations) H. A. Rey (borders) © Cockerell **275–284** George M. Ulrich **286–288** Ellen Walsh **285–303** Linda Phinney (borders) **294–296, 298–300** Mary Keefe

Photographers: **56** (top) Jeffrey Reed/Stock Shop **56** (bottom) © Dennis Black/Black Star **57** (left) © Bard Martin/The Image Bank **57** (right) Robert Frerck/Odyssey Productions **58** (left) McNally Wheeler/Wheeler Pictures **58** (right) Bohdan Hrynewych/Southern Light **59** (left) Focus on Sports **59** (right) © Frerik D. Dodin/Stock Boston **60** (right) © Michal Heron/Woodfin Camp **60** (left) © Stuart Cohen/Stock Boston **228** © John Launois/Black Star **229** © Steve Proehl/The Image Bank **230** (left) The Phelps Agency **230** (right) Photo Researchers, Inc. **231** Jules Bucher/Photo Researchers, Inc. **232** (left) © Lincoln Russell/Stock Boston **232** (right) Mike Phiccins/Peter Arnold, Inc. **285** Norman N. Thompson/Taurus Photos **294, 297, 300–302** Michal Heron